Stunning CGP practice for Year 9 Maths!

Year 9 is the final stretch of KS3 Maths, with plenty of challenges to look forward to. But don't worry — this CGP Workbook has all the practice you need for success.

Each section starts with warm-up questions to make sure you're ready to get started. After that, there's stacks of brilliant practice to build up those vital Maths skills. It's all split into topics, so it's easy to target anything you're finding tough.

And there's more... we've also included regular review exercises so you can check how you're doing, plus fully worked answers to every question. It's another winner from CGP!

CGP — still the best! ☺

Our sole aim here at CGP is to produce the highest quality books — carefully written, immaculately presented and dangerously close to being funny.

Then we work our socks off to get them out to you — at the cheapest possible prices.

Published by CGP

Editors:
Michael Bushell, Sarah George, Tom Miles, Rosa Roberts, Caley Simpson, Dawn Wright

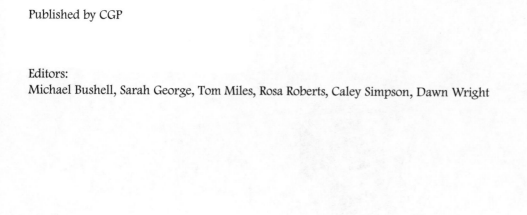

ISBN: 978 1 78908 318 7

With thanks to Alastair Duncombe and Glenn Rogers for the proofreading.

Clipart from Corel®
Printed by Elanders Ltd, Newcastle upon Tyne.

Based on the classic CGP style created by Richard Parsons.

Contents

How To Use This Book 2

Section One — Number

Before you Start 4
Number Problems 5
Rounding 7
Estimating 8
Rounding Errors 9
Power Laws 10
Standard Form 11
Prime Factors 13
Review Exercise 14

Section Two — Proportions and Units

Before you Start 16
Fraction Problems 17
Percentage Change 19
Ratios 21
Direct Proportion 23
Inverse Proportion 24
Speed 25
Density 26
Best Buy Problems 27
Metric and Imperial Conversions 29
Maps and Map Scales 30
Review Exercise 31

Section Three — Algebra and Graphs

Before you Start 33
Expanding Brackets 34
Factorising 35
Solving Equations 36
Inequalities 37
Formulas 39
Sequences 41
Finding the Equation of a Straight Line 42
Quadratic Graphs 44
Solving Equations Using Graphs 46
Real-Life Graphs 48
Review Exercise 50

Section Four — Geometry

Before you Start 52
Polygons 53
Loci and Constructions 55
Transformations 57
3D Shapes 60
Pythagoras' Theorem 62
Trigonometry 63
Similarity and Congruence 64
Geometric Relationships 65
Review Exercise 66

Section Five — Probability and Statistics

Before you Start 68
Probability from Experiments 69
Theoretical Probability 70
Displaying Data 72
Scatter Graphs 74
Averages and Range from Tables 75
Review Exercise 77

Answers 79
Topic Map 98

How To Use This Book

- Hold the book <u>upright</u>, approximately <u>50 cm</u> from your face, ensuring that the text looks like <u>this</u>, not this. Alternatively, place the book on a <u>horizontal</u> surface (e.g. a table or desk) and sit adjacent to the book, at a distance which doesn't make the text too small to read.

- In case of emergency, press the two halves of the book together <u>firmly</u> in order to close.

- Before attempting to use this book, familiarise yourself with the following <u>safety information</u>:

> Different schools teach Key Stage 3 Maths in a <u>slightly different order</u>. <u>Don't panic</u> if you come across something you haven't learned yet — just <u>skip</u> that topic and move on. If there's a topic <u>missing</u>, you'll probably find it in our <u>Year 7</u> or <u>Year 8</u> book. There's a table at the <u>back</u> of this book showing you where <u>everything</u> is <u>covered</u>.

> This book has <u>five sections</u> covering different areas of maths. Each section is split up into <u>topics</u>, so it's easy to find questions on a <u>specific thing</u> you want to <u>practise</u>.

> Every question in this book has a <u>fully worked solution</u> at the back — the answers start on page 79.

> There's <u>plenty of space</u> below each question for you to do your <u>working</u>. Then write your answer on the <u>dotted line</u>.

33

Section Three — Algebra and Graphs

So... you've found my hoard of questions on Algebra and Graphs — I knew you would one day. My next challenge for you is to find the answers (and I don't mean skipping to the answer page).

Before you Start

1. Expand the brackets in these expressions.

 $5(p + 6) =$ .... $2(7 - q) =$ ....

2. Fully factorise these expressions.

 $r - 15rs =$ .... $16t^2 - 8u =$ ....

3. Solve these equations.

 a) $3(x + 6) = 4x$ b) $\frac{36 - 4y}{2} = 6$

 $x =$ .... $y =$ ....

4. Anita places an empty 5000 ml bucket under a leaky roof.

 a) Every hour, the amount (l ml) of water in the bucket increases by 20 ml. Write down a formula for l after h hours have passed.

 ....

 b) How long does it take for the bucket to fill up?

 .... hours

5. Joshua writes down a sequence of numbers beginning: 17, 24, 31, 38, 45, ...

 a) Work out an expression for the nth term in the sequence.

 ....

 b) Calculate the 20th term.

 ....

6. Phoebe has found an ancient scroll showing a method to plot the graph of $y = 4x + 3$. Follow the instructions on the scroll to plot the graph.

 Fill in this table of values for $y = 4x + 3$.

x	0	1	2	3
y				

 Plot the points from your table and connect them with a straight line.

Section Three — Algebra and Graphs

> Each section starts with some <u>quick questions</u> to make sure you know <u>the basics</u> before launching in.

> <u>Calculators</u> are useful but you need to be able to solve problems <u>without</u> them too. You'll see questions in this book with this stamp next to them — this means you <u>can't use a calculator</u> for any part of the question. (You'll thank us one day...)

How To Use This Book

Each topic has a page or two of questions that get more challenging as you work through them.

Questions with blue boxes around the question number are a bit trickier than the others. These questions also test your problem-solving skills — you need to figure out what you have to do for yourself.

There are some hints to help you answer specific questions.

Each topic ends with a checklist. Tick off each point when you're happy you can do it. If there's anything you're unsure about, this is a good time to go back and have another look at it.

Direct Proportion

1. A recipe for four people requires two onions and six tomatoes.

   Ainsley wants to cook for 10 people.
   Shade the number of onions and tomatoes he will need.

2. Four chameleons can eat 340 bugs in a day.

   How many bugs can seven chameleons eat in a day?

   ....

3. A worker can pick 540 blackberries per hour.

   Tick the box beneath the graph which shows how many they can pick in t minutes.

4. 6 mechanics can perform a deluxe service on 3 cars in a day.

   a) How many days will it take 2 of the mechanics to perform this service on 5 cars?

   ....

   b) Let m represent the number of mechanics and c represent the number of cars serviced in a day. Write an equation in the form $c = km$ to represent this direct proportion.

   Find k by substituting the numbers in the question into the equation.

   ....

How did you do?

Page done. There's no beating about the bush with direct proportion... You should now be able to:

☐ Solve problems involving direct proportion.

☹☐ ☺☐ ☺☐

Section Two — Proportions and Units

Tick the box that matches how confident you feel with the topic. This should help to show you where you need to do a bit more practice.

Section Two — Review Exercise

Time to scale up your mental muscles and tackle the next two pages — that's right, you've reached the Review Exercise. On a scale from 'I got this' to 'No sweat', how ready do you feel?

1. Aaliyah is making up 16 party bags for her younger sister's birthday party.

   a) Aaliyah wants to put toys and sweets into the bags in the ratio 5:2.
   She has 80 toys. How many sweets does she need?

   .... ☐ *2 marks*

   b) (i) She cuts the birthday cake into 16 equal slices. After putting 15 of the slices into bags, she realises that she needs to make two extra party bags. She cuts the final slice into thirds.

   What fraction of the full cake goes into the final 3 party bags?

   .... ☐ *2 marks*

   (ii) Two of the guests are siblings. One of them gets one of the larger slices and the other gets one of the final three slices. What fraction of the cake do they have altogether? Give your answer in its simplest form.

   .... ☐ *1 mark*

2. A cinema's revenue in December increased by 45% compared to November. The revenue in December was £1740. What was the revenue in November?

   £ .... ☐ *2 marks*

3. Chas writes letters to his pen pal. He can write 690 words an hour.

   a) How many words can he write in 14 minutes?

   .... ☐ *2 marks*

   b) How long would it take him to write 1725 words?

   .... hours .... minutes ☐ *2 marks*

4. A group of backpackers decides to run a car wash to raise funds for a trip. 4 backpackers can clean 80 cars in a day.

   a) Given that each backpacker cleans at the same rate, how many backpackers would it take to clean 140 cars in a day?

   .... ☐ *2 marks*

   b) The backpackers get a new hose. 6 backpackers can now clean 144 cars in a day. How many days would it take 2 backpackers to clean 144 cars?

   .... ☐ *1 mark*

Section Two — Review Exercise

Once you've made it to the end of a section, have a go at the Review Exercise to test how much you remember. Each exercise has two pages of questions that cover the topics in the section.

Review questions have marks allocated to them — the worked solutions show what you need to do to get each mark.

Section One — Number

Section One covers the fundamentals of working with numbers — not a bold choice, but a sensible one. Have a go at the starter questions below to get prepped for what's coming up.

1. Briany is at a scrapyard buying parts to feed her dog Rex. The parts are sold in small bags (0.25 kg) costing £4.95 and large bags (1 kg) costing £17.15.

    a) Briany buys a number of small bags having a total mass of 4 kg.

        (i) How many bags did Briany buy? ~~16~~

        .... small bags

        (ii) How much did this cost? 79p

        £ 79.20

    b) How much could Briany save by buying the same mass in large bags?

    £ 10.60

2. Round:

    a) 3.056 to 2 decimal places

    3.06

    b) 1349 to 2 significant figures

    1300

3. By rounding each number to one significant figure, estimate the answer to: $4.34^2 - \sqrt{96.1} + 3.51 \div 1.87$

    8

4. Write these numbers as a power of ten or as a multiple of a power of ten. One has been done for you.

    $300 = \underline{3 \times 10^2}$ $1000 = 10^3$ $50\,000 = 5 \times 10\,000$

    5×10^{4}

5. Work out each number that is being described below.

    a) Its prime factorisation is $2^2 \times 3 \times 5$.

    60

    b) Its prime factors are 3 and 5. It is a three-digit square number.

    225

    $2^2 \times 3 \times 5 = 4 \times 15 = 60$

    $3^2 \times 5^2 = 9 \times 25 = 225$

Number Problems

1. Fill in the boxes to complete the following calculations.

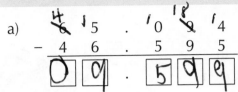

a)

```
    ⁴7̶  ¹5  .  ¹0  ¹8̶  ¹4
  -  4   6  .   5   9   5
  ─────────────────────
   [0][9]  .  [5][9][9]
```

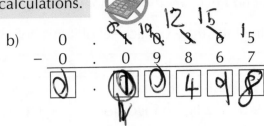

b)

```
    0  .  ⁰1̶  ¹⁹0̶  ¹²2̶  ¹⁵5̶  ¹5
  - 0  .   0    9    8   6   7
  ──────────────────────────
   [0]  .  [0][0][4][9][8]
```

2. An oil rig has a height of 74.98 m visible above water and extends 518.16 m below the surface to the sea floor. What is the total height of the oil rig?

```
   518.16 M
 + 74.98
 ─────────
   593.14
```

593.14 m

3. Dirk's calculator has a glitch where it doesn't display decimal points.

The result of the multiplication 8.17 × 31.02 is displayed below.

2534334

Write down the correct answer to Dirk's calculation.

253.4534

4. Salma is calculating using long division.

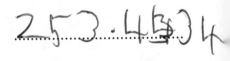

a) Fill in the boxes to complete Salma's calculation.

b) (i) Salma bought 13 tulips from a florist for £21.58. What was the cost of a single tulip?

£1.66

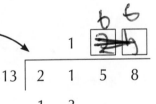

```
            1  [6][6]
        ──────────────
     13 │ 2  1  5  8
          1  3
        ──────────
         [8][8][5]
       - [0][7][8]
        ──────────
          [8][7][8]
        - [0][7][8]
        ──────────
             [0]
```

(ii) Later, the florist had a special offer of 5 tulips for £7.49. Single tulips cost the same. How much money could Salma have saved using this deal to buy 13 tulips?

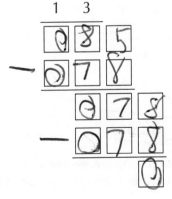

£1.62

Number Problems

5. Clark and Kevin are moving home and have split some items between them.

Find the total mass of each set of items below.

Clark	Kevin
3 6 . 2 8 kg Bookcase	5 4 . 5 1 kg Oven
9 0 . 7 2 kg Refrigerator	1 1 5 . 3 9 kg Washing Machine
2 7 5 . 5 0 kg Dumbbell Set	2 3 6 . 7 9 kg Security Safe
.... kg Total	.... kg Total

Who is moving the heavier set of items?   Tick your answer: Clark ☐   Kevin ✓

6. Brand A sells dog food in 0.4 kg cans, with 24 cans costing £12.
Brand B sells dog food in 0.35 kg cans, with 6 cans costing £2.52.

By comparing the cost per kg, say which brand of dog food is cheaper.

Brand ....

7. Six negative numbers have fallen off the calculations below: –2, –3, –4, –5, –10, –11.

Fill in the boxes by putting the numbers back in their rightful places.

$$\frac{\boxed{} \div \boxed{}}{5} = 1$$

$$\frac{5 - \boxed{}}{\boxed{} + 8} = 2$$

$$\frac{-(\boxed{}) \times 2}{6 + \boxed{}} = 11$$

How did you do?

Number problems are the bread and butter of mathematics — they make pretty boring sandwiches on their own, but they're often filled with other tasty topics. So check that you can:

☐ Add and subtract using whole and decimal numbers, both positive and negative.

☐ Multiply and divide using whole and decimal numbers, both positive and negative.

    ☐   ☐   ☐

Rounding

1. Fill in the gaps below.

1.6962 = **1.70** to 2 d.p.

0.4247 = 0.425 to **3** d.p.

0.007395 = 0.007 to **3** d.p.

0.007395 = **0.0074** to 4 d.p.

2. Round these numbers to the given number of significant figures.

32 549 = **32500** to 3 s.f.

32 549 = **32550** to 4 s.f.

909 520 = **910000** to 3 s.f.

909 520 = **909500** to 4 s.f.

3. Complete the table by rounding each number to 3, 4 and 5 significant figures.

	3 s.f.	4 s.f.	5 s.f.
825 624	826000	825 600	825620
13.2973	13.3	13.30	13.297
0.094069	0.0941	0.09407	0.094069

4. On a rainy weekend, Miki claims to have spent a total of 30 000 seconds watching TV.

Suppose this time is correct to 3 significant figures. Which of the following could be the actual time for which Miki watched TV? Circle all possible answers.

29 000 s   29 500 s   (29 999 s)   (30 049 s)   30 100 s

5. Avril is trying to push a bookcase through a doorway.

The bookcase has a height of 2.00 m to 3 s.f. and the doorway has a height of exactly 1.95 m. Is it possible to fit the bookcase through the doorway, keeping it upright and without tilting it? Explain your answer.

No — the smallest possible height of the bookcase is 1.995m, which is greater than 1.95 m

Estimating

1. Alex goes to a funfair. A list of prices is shown on the right.

Alex rides on the waltzer twice, the roller coaster once and plays the hoop game five times. He also buys one bag of candyfloss.

By rounding all prices to 1 s.f., estimate the total amount of money that Alex spent.

 £ .18.....

Hoop game:	£1.50
Haunted house:	£1.85
Roller coaster:	£2.95
Waltzer:	£2.10
Candyfloss:	£0.70
Popcorn:	£0.90

2. By rounding all numbers to 2 s.f., estimate the following values.

Give your answers as fractions or mixed numbers.

a) $x = \dfrac{\sqrt{36.05}}{5.019}$

b) $y = \dfrac{\sqrt[3]{63.71}}{(3.04)^2}$

$x \approx$ ....

$y \approx$ ....

3. Chantel has used approximate values to find the estimates below.

For each part, tick whether Chantel has rounded the numbers in her calculations to 1 d.p. or to 1 s.f.

a) $0.289 \times 0.05 \approx 0.03$

 1 d.p. ☐ 1 s.f.

b) $0.067 \times 0.44 \approx 0.028$

☐ 1 d.p. 1 s.f.

c) $1.531 \times 0.63 \approx 1.2$

☐ 1 d.p. 1 s.f.

4. The spacefaring aliens of planet Estimat are planning to beam up the entire human population of the UK. Estimate how many cargo vessels they would need.

Use the fact that the population of the UK is 66.04 million and a single cargo vessel holds 4900 humans.

Round each number to 1 s.f.

.... 14000 cargo vessels

How did you do?

Don't confuse estimations with Estimatians — the latter just beamed up Steve from down the road. After working through this page, you should be able to:

☐ Use approximate values to estimate the answers to calculations.

 ☐ ☐ ☐

Rounding Errors

1. Calculate the error when 12.546 is rounded to:

a) 2 s.f.

0.454

b) 2 d.p.

0.004

2. Complete the following table of rounding errors.

Actual number	Rounded number	Rounding error
124.65	125 to 3 s.f.	0.35
0.4318	0.432 to ___ s.f.	0.0002
7.5391	7.5 to 2 s.f.	0.0391

3. Naomi and Peta go for a walk.

Naomi walked 4560 m to the nearest 10 m. Peta walked 4600 m to the nearest 100 m.

a) Write down the range of possible values for the actual length, n, of Naomi's walk and the actual length, p, of Peta's walk.

.... m ≤ n < .... m

.... m ≤ p < .... m

b) Tick all of the following statements that **could** be true.

[✓] Naomi walked further than Peta.   [✓] Peta walked further than Naomi.

[✓] Naomi and Peta walked exactly the same distance.

4. Write down the range of possible values for the following rounded numbers.

Give each of your answers as an inequality.

a) $x = 120$ to the nearest 10

4555 m ≤ n < 4565 m

b) $y = 1.24$ to 2 d.p.

....

c) $z = 0.0124$ to 3 s.f.

....

Power Laws

1. What is the expression $2^3 \times 2^4$ equal to? Circle your answer.

$2^3 + 2^4$ $2^{3 \times 4}$ (circled) $(3 + 4)^2$ 2^{3+4} $(2^3)^4$

2. Fill in the boxes to simplify each of these calculations.

$5^2 \times 5^3 = 5^{\boxed{5}}$

$6^4 \times 6^{\boxed{6}} = 6^{10}$

$4 \times 2^7 = 2^{\boxed{9}}$

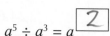 Start by writing 4 as a power of 2.

$3^6 \div 3^2 = 3^{\boxed{4}}$

$3^a \div 3^{\boxed{2}} = 3^{a-2}$

$a^5 \div a^3 = a^{\boxed{2}}$

3. Use power laws to simplify these expressions, leaving your answers as powers.

a) $\dfrac{7^4 \times 7^6}{7^5}$

7^5

b) $(3^7 \div 3^2)^4$

3^{20}

4. Which of the expressions below is the odd one out? Underline your answer.

x^6 $x^2 \times x^4$ $(x^2)^3$ $x^8 \div x^2$ $x^2 \times x^3$ $x^3 \times x^3$

5. Which of these calculations are true (☑) and which are false (☒)?

$5^1 \div 5^1 = 1$ ✓ $5^1 \div 5^1 = 5^0$ ✓ $5^0 = 0$ ✗ $5^0 = 1$ ✓

6. Power laws work with negative powers.

a) Fill in the boxes to complete this calculation.

$$10^{-2} = 10^0 \div 10^{\boxed{2}} = \frac{1}{10^{\boxed{2}}} = \frac{1}{\boxed{100}}$$

b) Which of these is the correct power law? Part a) is an example of it. Circle your answer.

$10^{-n} = \dfrac{n}{10}$ (crossed out/circled) $10^{-n} = \dfrac{1}{10^n}$ (circled) $10^{-n} = -10^n$

How did you do?

Power laws are... well, powerful — so be sure to tuck them away in your algebra tool kit. They work with negative powers too, and you'll be seeing these on the next page — so check you can:

☐ Use power laws to simplify expressions, including those with negative powers.

Standard Form

1. Which of these numbers is 1.2×10^3 as an ordinary number? Circle your answer.

| 1.2000 | | 12 | | 120 | | 1200 | | 12 000 |

2. Fill in the boxes to write these numbers in standard form.

$200\ 000 = \boxed{} \times 10^{\boxed{}}$
    $54\ 000 = \boxed{} \times 10^{\boxed{}}$
    $127\ 000 = \boxed{} \times 10^{\boxed{}}$

3. The Earth is approximately 149 000 000 km away from the Sun.

Write this distance in standard form.

.... km

4. Convert these numbers from standard form to ordinary decimals.

Remember:
$10^{-n} = \dfrac{1}{10^n}$

The first one has been done for you.

$1.8 \times 10^{-1} = \underline{\ 0.18\ }$
    $2.5 \times 10^{-2} = \dots\dots\dots\dots$
    $3.84 \times 10^{-3} = \dots\dots\dots\dots$

5. Write these numbers in standard form.

$0.05 = \dots\dots\dots\dots$
    $0.807 = \dots\dots\dots\dots$
    $0.00261 = \dots\dots\dots\dots$

6. The world's smallest known insect* has been known to have a body length of as little as 0.000139 m.

Write this length in standard form.

.... m

7. Stanley is throwing a number party. Only numbers in standard form are allowed in.

a) Circle the numbers that are **not** written in standard form.

0.6×10^6

8×10^{-5}

0.54×10^{-12}

8.6×10^9

10×10^3

1×10^2

44×10^7

b) Write each number that you've circled above in standard form.

....

*A male *dicopomorpha echmepterygis* fairyfly

Standard Form

8. Write these numbers in order from smallest to largest.

Leave each number in standard form.

$$1.2 \times 10^5 \qquad 1.2 \times 10^{-5} \qquad 1.2 \times 10^6 \qquad 2.1 \times 10^5 \qquad 2.1 \times 10^{-6}$$

...................., ..., ..., ..., ...

9. The colour of light depends on its wavelength.

You don't need to know the science to answer this question. Work with the given numbers.

a) Fill in this table showing the wavelength of different colours.

Colour	Wavelength	Standard Form
Red (R)	0.000000685 m	.... m
Green (G)	.... m	5.2×10^{-7} m
Blue (B)	0.00000046 m	.... m

b) Yellow (Y) light has a wavelength of 5.8×10^{-7} m. Which of these sequences is the correct order of these colours, from the smallest to largest wavelength? Circle your answer.

B Y G R   B G Y R   R G Y B   R Y G B

10. Work out these calculations.

$(3 \times 10^2) \times (2 \times 10^3)$ = ... × 10...... $(6 \times 10^6) \div (2 \times 10^3)$ = ... × 10......

11. Riad wants to calculate 0.002 × 0.0004.

a) Use power laws to write $10^{-3} \times 10^{-4}$ as a single power of 10.   ....

b) (i) Calculate $(2 \times 10^{-3}) \times (4 \times 10^{-4})$.   (ii) Write down 0.002 × 0.0004
Write your answer in standard form.   as a decimal number.

....

How did you do?

From zero to hero — you're all done. Standard form is useful for writing down very big and very small numbers, as well as for doing calculations with such numbers. You should be able to:

☐ Change between ordinary and standard form for large numbers.

☐ Change between ordinary and standard form for small numbers.

☐ Compare and order numbers in standard form.   ☐ Calculate with numbers in standard form.

           ☐   ☐   ☐

Prime Factors

1. Reggie thinks that 1156 is a square number.

a) Complete the factor tree on the right.

b) Is Reggie correct? Explain your answer.

....

....

The branches of factor trees must end with primes.

2. The prime factorisation of 29 791 000 is $2^3 \times 5^3 \times 31^3$.

What is the value of $\sqrt[3]{29\ 791\ 000}$? Circle your answer.

| 38 | 310 | 2531 | 29 791 | 96 100 |

3. Factor trees for the numbers 198, 390 and 462 have been partially filled in below.

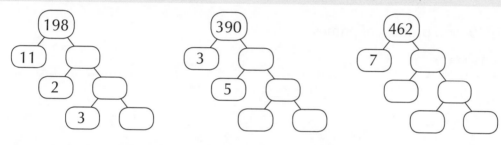

a) Complete each factor tree and then write each number as a product of primes.

198 = ... 390 = ... 462 = ...

b) What is the highest common factor of 198, 390 and 462? ....

4. Complete these prime factorisations and use them to work out the lowest common multiple of each pair.

a) 105 = 3 × ...... × 7 and 110 = 2 × ...... × 11

The LCM of 105 and 110 is ....

b) 156 = ...^{2} × 3 × 13 and 234 = 2 × ......^{2} × 13

The LCM of 156 and 234 is ....

How did you do?

Did you know: seven and eleven are prhyme numbers? I made that up. But you should know how to:

☐ Use prime factorisation to identify types of numbers, e.g. squares and cubes.

☐ Use prime factorisation to solve number problems, e.g. finding HCFs and LCMs.

 ☐   ☐   ☐

Section One — Review Exercise

Flick back through this section — if there's a checkbox left unticked, then you've got a gap to fill in your knowledge. If not, superb — you're 100% primed for this Review Exercise.

1. Leona's favourite number is 7429.

a) (i) Calculate $M = 7429 \div 19$.

$$19 \overline{)7429}$$

(ii) By rounding each number to 1 s.f., estimate:

$13 \times 17 \approx \ldots \times \ldots = \ldots$

$17 \times 23 \approx \ldots \times \ldots = \ldots$

$17 \times 29 \approx \ldots \times \ldots = \ldots$

1 mark

3 marks

(iii) One of these is the exact value of M. Which is it? Circle your answer.

$\boxed{13 \times 17}$ $\boxed{17 \times 23}$ $\boxed{17 \times 29}$

1 mark

b) Write 7429^3 as a product of primes.

Hint: $7429 = M \times 19$

....

2 marks

2. A number, N, is rounded to 3 significant figures. The result is 1.05.
What is the range of possible values of N?
Use inequality notation in your answer.

....

2 marks

3. Use power laws to simplify these expressions, leaving your answers as powers of 2.

a) $\dfrac{2^6 \times 2^2}{2^3}$

$= 2^{\boxed{}}$

b) $\dfrac{2^6}{(2^2)^9}$

$= 2^{\boxed{}}\ \boxed{}$

2 marks

4. Xel'Trev, from the planet Estimat, owns three spaceships. The table below shows the fuel capacity of each ship. Write each of these numbers in standard form.

	Escape pod	Cargo vessel	Battle cruiser
Fuel capacity	142 L	65 100 L	7 080 000 L
Standard form	.... × 10······ L	.... × 10······ L	.... × 10······ L

3 marks

Section One — Review Exercise

5. Write these numbers in order from smallest to largest.

4.3×10^{-3} 0.00024 3.4×10^{-3} 0.23 3.2×10^{-4}

........................, ..., ..., ..., ...

1 mark

6. Abdur thinks that 52×637 is a square number.

a) (i) Calculate 52×637.

$$\begin{array}{r} 6\ 3\ 7 \\ \times\quad 5\ 2 \\ \hline \square\ \square\ \square\ \square \\ +\ \square\ \square\ \square\ \square \\ \hline \square\ \square\ \square\ \square \end{array}$$

(ii) Write 52 and 637 as a product of prime numbers.

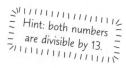
Hint: both numbers are divisible by 13.

2 marks

$52 = \ldots \times \ldots \times \ldots$ $637 = \ldots \times \ldots \times \ldots$

4 marks

(iii) Explain why Abdur is correct.

....

....

1 mark

b) Calculate $\sqrt{52 \times 637}$.

....

2 marks

7. A comet passes Earth every 70 years. Another comet passes Earth every 75 years. If both comets pass Earth this year, how many years will it be before they both pass Earth on the same year again?

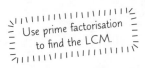
Use prime factorisation to find the LCM.

.... years

3 marks

Chilling with aliens isn't an excuse for not studying...

...unless you snapped a selfie in space — that, I'll accept as proof. Mark these questions and don't be too generous. If you haven't quite got the full answer, keep trying... you'll get there in the end.

Score:

27

Section Two — Proportions and Units

Now *this* is where the fun really starts. This section's got fractions, it's got ratios, it's got percentages, it's got speed, it's even got scales. If you want some proportions and units, this is where you need to be.

Before you Start

1. Work out the following, giving your answers as mixed numbers:

   a) $\frac{3}{5} + \frac{1}{2}$ 4 b) $\frac{3}{4} \div \frac{5}{9}$ 27

   .... 7 ....

   20

2. A bag originally costs £24. It goes on sale and now has 35% off. How much does the bag cost in the sale?

   £ ....

3. The ratio of ants to woodlice on a log is 20:4.

   a) Write the ratio in its simplest form.

   .... : ....

   b) There are 50 ants on the log. How many woodlice are there?

   ....

4. A car travels 156 miles in 3 hours. What is the car's average speed?

   .... mph

5. Evelyn can make 4 gift boxes using 28 chocolates.

   a) How many chocolates does she need to make 10 of these gift boxes?

   ....

   b) How many of these gift boxes can she make using 42 chocolates?

   ....

6. Write 2 feet 6 inches in cm.

   1 foot = 12 inches ≈ 30 cm

   .... cm

7. Duncan is building a scale model of a piano using the scale 1 cm = 6 cm.

   If the width of the model piano is 20 cm, what is the width of the actual piano?

   .... cm

Fraction Problems

1. Work out the following, giving your answers in their simplest form.

   a) $\frac{1}{5} + 1\frac{1}{3}$

   b) $\frac{5}{6} - \frac{3}{4}$

   ....

   $\frac{2}{2}$

   ....

   c) $1\frac{3}{7} \times \frac{2}{5}$

   d) $\frac{2}{9} \div 1\frac{1}{3}$

   ....

   ....

2. Mary and 11 of her friends vote on whether to go to the park or to play board games.

   $\frac{1}{3}$ vote to play board games and $\frac{1}{6}$ refuse to vote. No one votes for more than one option.

   a) What fraction of them vote to go to the park? Simplify your answer.

   ....

   b) While they are deciding, it begins to rain. They take a new vote.
   Now $\frac{3}{4}$ vote to play board games and only one doesn't vote.
   What fraction of them vote to go to the park this time?

   ....

3. Sanjay, Malcolm, Sarah and Christie share $\frac{2}{5}$ of a casserole equally between them.

   What fraction of the casserole does each person get? Simplify your answer.

   ....

4. Paul owns a collection of action figures. $\frac{3}{8}$ of his collection are superheroes.
   Of the ones that are superheroes, $\frac{1}{4}$ of them have capes.

   a) What fraction of Paul's collection are cape-wearing superheroes?

   ....

   b) $\frac{2}{3}$ of the action figures which aren't superheroes are in mint condition.
   What fraction of Paul's collection are in mint condition and not superheroes?
   Simplify your answer.

   ....

Section Two — Proportions and Units

Fraction Problems

5. Enrique and Joey both love red.

$\frac{4}{9}$ of Enrique's clothes are red and 62.5% of Joey's clothes are red.

a) Who owns the greater proportion of red clothes?

....

b) Enrique has 108 items of clothing in total. He gives away $\frac{1}{6}$ of his red clothes to charity. How many items of clothing does he give away?

....

6. On Wednesday, Gabrielle swam 0.8 km. On Friday, she swam $2\frac{3}{4}$ times as far.

How many kilometres did she swim on Friday?
Write your answer as a mixed number in its simplest form.

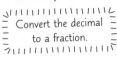
Convert the decimal to a fraction.

.... km

7. To escape this page, you need to find the combination to open this padlock.

Find the value of each symbol (☆ and ○) by solving the calculations.
Then use these in the final two calculations and write your answers as simplified improper fractions in the padlock.

$$\text{☆} = 1\frac{5}{12} - \frac{1}{4} \qquad \text{○} = 1\frac{1}{8} - \frac{11}{24}$$

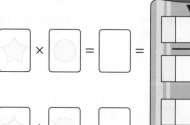

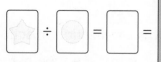

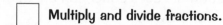

How did you do?

... And you've made it out! What fraction of you wants to do that all again? $\frac{10}{10}$? I thought so.
Before you move on to the next page, make sure that you can:

☐ Add and subtract fractions.   ☐ Multiply and divide fractions.

☐ Convert between fractions, percentages and decimals.

Percentage Change

1. Tom has a badge collection. He buys more so that his collection increases by 35%.

   He originally had 20 badges. How many badges does he have now?

   ....

2. Cecilia went for a run on both Saturday and Sunday.
   On Sunday, she ran 60% further than she did on Saturday.

   Cecilia ran 3900 m on Saturday. How far did she run on Sunday?

   .... m

3. Tamara eats 90% of the chips on her plate. There are now four chips left.

   How many chips did she have to start with?

   ....

4. Jasper starts the day with a full bottle of water.

   a) By lunchtime, he has drunk 30% of the water and now has 665 ml of water left.
      How much water was in Jasper's bottle when it was full?

   .... ml

   b) In the afternoon, he drinks a further 20% of the original amount of water.
      How many millilitres did he drink in the afternoon?

   .... ml

5. A department store is having a sale. Match the offers with the percentage discount.

Was £60
Now £39

Was £65
Now £39

Was £44
Now £22

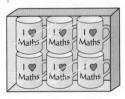

Was £30
Now £12

| 50% off | 60% off | 35% off | 40% off |

Percentage Change

6. One month, a charity receives £1250 in donations.
The next month, after a fundraiser, the charity receives £2200 in donations.

By what percentage did the donations increase from the first month to the next?

To find a percentage change, divide the difference in the amounts by the original amount, then multiply by 100.

.... %

7. Brighter Days Bank offers an account that pays 2% simple interest each year.

2% simple interest means 2% of the original amount of money in the account is added each year.

Save your way to a brighter day!
Earn 2% simple interest
THIS WAY

a) Oliver opens an account with £300.

(i) How much money will he have earned in interest after one year?

£ ....

(ii) How much money will he have earned in interest after three years?

£ ....

b) Emily opens an account with £500.

(i) How much money will she have earned in interest after one year?

£ ....

(ii) How much will be in her account after two years?

£ ....

8. Jamila invests £2500 in a savings account. After a year, she has earned £75 in simple interest.

a) What percentage interest does the account pay?

What percentage of £2500 is £75?

.... %

b) Jamila opens a different account with £1000. It pays 1.5% simple interest.
How much will be in the account two years from now?

£ ....

How did you do?

My brother is intrigued by percentages, but he doesn't like the complicated bits
— it's only a simple interest... Once you've stopped laughing (or rolling your eyes), see if you can:

☐ Find amounts before and after a percentage change.   ☐ Work with simple interest rates.

☐ Find the percentage change when given the amounts before and after the change.

Ratios

1. Simplify the following ratios.

   a) $6:30$

       .... : ....

   b) $18:27$

       .... : ....

2. A 250 g bag of flour is split between two recipes in the ratio $3:2$.

Write down below how many grams of flour each recipe will use.

.... g   .... g

3. The ratio of clocks to lamps in a library is $2:5$.

There are 15 lamps. How many clocks are there?

....

4. A running club meets on Tuesdays and Thursdays.
Each member of the club is either a long-distance runner or a sprinter.

   a) On Tuesdays, there are four times as many long-distance runners as sprinters.
Write the ratio of long-distance runners to sprinters on Tuesdays in its simplest form.

       .... : ....

   b) On Thursdays, the ratio of long-distance runners to sprinters is $3:7$.
What fraction of the members meeting on Thursdays are long-distance runners?

       ....

5. 63 guests are invited to Florence and Lewis's wedding.

The ratio of Florence's guests to Lewis's guests is $4:5$.

   a) How many of the guests did Florence invite?

       ....

   b) 8 of Florence's guests and 3 of Lewis's guests can't make it.
Write the new ratio of Florence's guests to Lewis's guests in its simplest form.

       .... : ....

Section Two — Proportions and Units

Ratios

6. Solveig has a bag of 30 sweets.

The ratio of liquorice sweets to all the sweets in the bag is $1:3$.

a) How many of the sweets are liquorice?

....

b) Solveig eats 4 liquorice sweets and 5 non-liquorice sweets.
What is the new ratio of liquorice sweets to all the sweets in its simplest form?

.... : ....

7. The ratio of pizza dishes to pasta dishes offered in an Italian restaurant is $1:1.25$ when written in the form $1:n$.

There are 12 pizza dishes.

a) How many pasta dishes are there?

You can multiply both sides of the ratio by 4 to get rid of the decimal part.

....

b) The restaurant offers 5 dishes which are neither pizza nor pasta.
What is the ratio of pizza dishes to all non-pizza dishes on offer?
Write the ratio in its simplest form.

.... : ....

8. Two wind-up toys are raced against each other.

The distances they travel are in the ratio 80 cm : 2 m.

a) Reduce the ratio to its simplest form.

Convert the distances to the same units and then reduce the ratio to its simplest form. Leave the units out of the final answer.

.... : ....

b) Write this ratio in the form $1:n$.

.... : ....

How did you do?

Wind-up toys really get on my nerves... I think some more maths will calm me down.
Before you get too wound up yourself, check that you can:

☐ Find amounts from ratios and solve problems involving ratios.

☐ Reduce ratios to their simplest form, including when they involve decimals or units.

Direct Proportion

1. A recipe for four people requires two onions and six tomatoes.

Ainsley wants to cook for 10 people.
Shade the number of onions and tomatoes he will need.

2. Four chameleons can eat 340 bugs in a day.

How many bugs can seven chameleons eat in a day?

....

3. A worker can pick 540 blackberries per hour.

Tick the box beneath the graph which shows how many they can pick in t minutes.

(graphs with Blackberries vs Time (t minutes), each with a tick box below)

4. 6 mechanics can perform a deluxe service on 3 cars in a day.

a) How many days will it take 2 of the mechanics to perform this service on 5 cars?

....

b) Let m represent the number of mechanics and c represent the number of cars serviced in a day. Write an equation in the form $c = km$ to represent this direct proportion.

Find k by substituting the numbers in the question into the equation.

....

How did you do?

Page done. There's no beating about the bush with direct proportion... You should now be able to:

☐ Solve problems involving direct proportion.

Inverse Proportion

1. It takes 5 cooks 2 hours to make a giant jelly. They then leave it to set.

   a) How many hours would it take one cook to make the jelly?

                                   .... hours

   b) How many minutes would it take 12 cooks to make the same jelly?

                                   .... minutes

2. 8 artists can paint the ceiling of a chapel in 24 days.

   a) How long would it take one artist to paint the ceiling?

                                   .... days

   b) How long would it take 12 artists to paint the same ceiling 3 times over?

                                   .... days

3. It takes 10 builders 8 months to build a house.

   a) Given that the builders all work at the same rate, how many months would it take 4 builders to build the same house?

                                   .... months

   b) Let b represent the number of builders and m represent the number of months. Write an equation in the form $m = \frac{k}{b}$ to represent the inverse proportion.

> Find k by substituting the numbers in the question into the equation.

                                   ....

4. 15 fruit-pickers can pick 2400 apples in 20 minutes.

   a) How long would it take 25 fruit-pickers to pick the same number of apples?

                                   .... minutes

   b) Let p be the number of fruit-pickers and t be the number of minutes it takes to pick 2400 apples. Write an equation in the form $t = \frac{k}{p}$ to represent the inverse proportion.

                                   ....

How did you do?

They say the more you learn, the less you know — except for maths, of course... So check you can:

☐ Solve problems involving inverse proportion.

Speed

1. A footballer sprints down the length of a 90 m pitch in 18 seconds.

Circle their speed in m/s.

     7 m/s   5 mph   0.2 m/s   2 mph   5 m/s

2. An otter swims at a speed of 0.4 m/s.

  a) How far can it swim in 45 seconds?

.... m

  b) How far can it swim in 5 minutes?

.... m

3. It takes a gaggle of geese 2 hours and 15 minutes to fly 99 miles.

  a) What was the average speed of the geese in mph?

.... mph

  b) How long would it take for the geese to fly 70 miles at the same speed?
     Give your answer to the nearest minute.

.... minutes

4. Yvette wants to catch a bus that leaves at 8:20 pm.

She sets off from her friend's house at 8:07 pm and walks at an average speed of 6.6 km/h.
Her friend lives 1650 metres from the bus stop.

  a) How long does it take Yvette to reach the bus stop?

.... minutes

  b) Does she reach the bus stop in time to catch the bus?
     Circle the correct answer.   Yes / No

How did you do?

"Gary, I don't think we're going the right way..."
Oh Gary — he does this every year. By now you should:

☐ Know the formula that links speed, distance and time.

☐ Be able to substitute values into the formula to solve speed problems.

Density

On this page, you'll need the formula

$$\text{density} = \frac{\text{mass}}{\text{volume}}$$

1. The density of cork is 0.24 g/cm³.

If a cork stopper from a bottle has a volume of 19.6 cm³, what is its mass in grams to 1 d.p.?

.... g

2. An iron bar has a mass of 7500 g and a density of 7.87 g/cm³.

What is the volume of the iron bar in cm³ to 2 s.f.?

.... cm³

3. A paddling pool can be filled with up to 1.28 m³ of water. When completely full, the total mass of the pool and the water is 1285 kg. When empty, the pool has a mass of 5 kg.

a) Use this information to find the density of water.

Start by working out the mass of the water in the pool.

.... kg/m³

b) The pool is partially filled so that the volume of water in the pool is 0.95 m³. What is the mass of the water?

.... kg

4. A sculpture is being built out of steel and concrete.

a) The steel frame of the sculpture is built with a volume of 0.2 m³. Steel has a density of 8050 kg/m³. Calculate the mass of the steel frame.

.... kg

b) Concrete is then added and fixed around the frame. The mass of the concrete is 4800 kg and its density is 2400 kg/m³.

(i) Calculate the volume of the concrete.

.... m³

(ii) What is the total volume of the sculpture?

.... m³

How did you do?

This page shouldn't make you feel dense... You can use the formula triangle to help you remember the formula for density — just like you do for speed. Right, make sure that you:

☐ Know the formula that links density, mass and volume.

☐ Can substitute values into the formula to solve density problems.

Best Buy Problems

1. Fruit 'n' Stuff sells bananas in packs of five for 90p.
Peelies sells bananas individually for 16p.

At which shop are bananas better value for money?

....

2. Bursting with Balloons are having a sale. They have three offers available.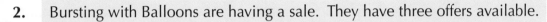

a) Match each offer with the corresponding price per balloon.

Small bundle: 3 balloons for £12   £3.75 per balloon

Medium bundle: 5 balloons for £18   £4 per balloon

Big bundle: 8 balloons for £30   £3.60 per balloon

b) Which bundle represents the best value for money?

....

3. A shop sells pasta in three different sizes.

a) Circle the packet which represents the best value for money.

300 g for 49p   500 g for 75p   1 kg for £1.60

b) Hassan has £5. He buys as many packets of the best value pasta as possible.
How much pasta does he buy in grams?

.... g

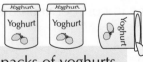

4. Foody Favourites and Dairy Delights sell packs of yoghurts.

Foody Favourites sells packs of 6 for £1.26. Dairy Delights sells packs of 8 for £1.76.
In which shop are yoghurts better value for money? Show your working.

Section Two — Proportions and Units

Best Buy Problems

5. Miriam and Dexter want to rent some roller skates. The rental company offers two deals.

Deal 1: £15 for 2 hours, then 8p for each extra minute.
Deal 2: 12p per minute.

a) Miriam rents some roller skates for 2 hours.
Which deal offers her the better value?

....

b) Dexter rents the skates for 2 hours 45 minutes.
Should he choose the same deal as Miriam? Show your working.

Yes / No

6. James wants to buy some pots of dip for a party.

Shop A sells each pot of dip for £1.20.
Shop B sells each pot of dip for £1.50 or 2 for £2.20.

a) Which shop is the better value for money if James buys 9 pots? Tick your answer.

Shop A ☐   Shop B ☐

b) James has time to go to both shops.
Show below how he can buy 9 pots of dip for exactly £10.

7. Two video streaming services have special offers for new customers.

Kickback Flicks offers one month of free service. It then costs £6.50 a month.
Amazing TV Time offers three months of free service. It then costs £7.80 a month.

a) Ceara wants to sign up to a streaming service for 12 months.
Which service will be the better value for money? Show your working.

....

b) Zac wants to sign up to a streaming service for 24 months.
Work out the difference in cost between the two services for this amount of time.

£ ....

How did you do?

Which is the better buy — this workbook or those beautiful shoes over there?
This book of course! Now you've done all that shopping, you should:

☐ Be able to compare values to find the option which represents the better value for money.

Section Two — Proportions and Units

Metric and Imperial Conversions

1. Fill in the gaps to complete the conversions.

1.75 hours = ☐ minutes = ☐ seconds   4.5 kg ≈ ☐ pounds   ⌇ 1 pound ≈ 450 g ⌇

374 mm = ☐ cm = ☐ m   32 pints = ☐ gallons   ⌇ 1 gallon = 8 pints ⌇

2. Darryl weighs some packages using the scales below. The total mass of the packages on the right-hand side is no less than the total mass of the packages on the left-hand side.

What is the minimum possible mass of the mystery box in grams?
Use the conversion 1 lb ≈ 0.45 kg.

⌇ lb is the symbol for pound. ⌇

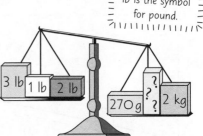

.... g

3. Joan is a big fan of the postal service and wants to convert some measurements.

a) She finds that the area of a stamp is 500 mm².
What is the area of the stamp in cm²?

⌇ Remember: 1 cm² = 10 mm × 10 mm ⌇

.... cm²

b) Joan knows that the capacity of a postbox is 0.204 m³.
What is the capacity of the postbox in cm³?

⌇ Remember: 1 m³ = 100 cm × 100 cm × 100 cm ⌇

.... cm³

4. Yasmina cycles to work at an average speed of 18 km/h.

a) How many metres would she cycle in 1 hour at this speed?

.... m

b) What is her speed in metres per second?

⌇ There are 3600 seconds in 1 hour. ⌇

.... m/s

How did you do?

The trick to doing well in maths is figuring out how to convert brain power into correct answers.
Plus lots of practice and hard work too of course, but that bit isn't as fun. You should be able to:

☐ Convert between different units of measurement.

 ☐   ☐   ☐

Maps and Map Scales

1. Heather builds a model of a park using the scale 1:50.

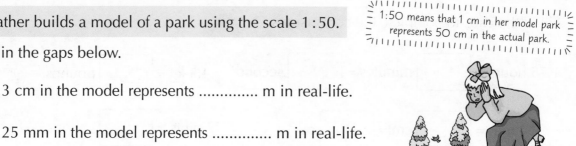

1:50 means that 1 cm in her model park represents 50 cm in the actual park.

Fill in the gaps below.

3 cm in the model represents .... m in real-life.

25 mm in the model represents .... m in real-life.

.... mm in the model represents 35 cm in real-life.

2. A road from A to B is shown on the map below. It is 72 km long.

72 km

a) Measure the road to find the scale of the map. Write your answer in the form 1 cm = n km.

....

b) Write your answer from part a) in the form 1 : n.

....

c) The town of Tootins lies 36 km away from point A on a bearing of 065°. Mark the location of Tootins on the map with a cross.

The bearing is the clockwise angle from the north line.

3. The map below shows the location of two villages.

a) Plumstone is 24 miles west of Webberly. Mark the location of Plumstone on the map with a cross.

b) (i) Find the real-life distance from Tilldon to Webberly.

.... miles

(ii) Measure the bearing of Webberly from Tilldon.

....................°

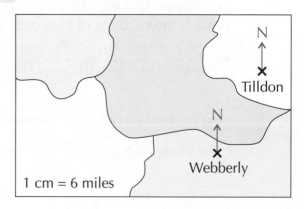

Tilldon

Webberly

1 cm = 6 miles

How did you do?

That's the end of the last topic — I hope you didn't get too lost. By now, you should be able to:

☐ Use scale factors to work out real-life distances.

☐ Use bearings on maps.

☐ Understand scales given in ratio form.

 ☐ ☐ ☐

Section Two — Review Exercise

1. Aaliyah is making up 16 party bags for her younger sister's birthday party.

   a) Aaliyah wants to put toys and sweets into the bags in the ratio 5:2.
      She has 80 toys. How many sweets does she need?

      .... ☐
      2 marks

   b) (i) She cuts the birthday cake into 16 equal slices. After putting 15 of the
          slices into bags, she realises that she needs to make two extra party bags.
          She cuts the final slice into thirds.

          What fraction of the full cake goes into the final 3 party bags?

          .... ☐
          2 marks

      (ii) Two of the guests are siblings. One of them gets one of the larger slices and
           the other gets one of the final three slices. What fraction of the cake do they
           have altogether? Give your answer in its simplest form.

           .... ☐
           1 mark

2. A cinema's revenue in December increased by 45% compared to November.
   The revenue in December was £1740. What was the revenue in November?

   £ .... ☐
   2 marks

3. Chas writes letters to his pen pal. He can write 690 words an hour.

   a) How many words can he write in 14 minutes?

      .... ☐
      2 marks

   b) How long would it take him to write 1725 words?

      .... hours .... minutes ☐
      2 marks

4. A group of backpackers decides to run a car wash to raise funds for a trip.
   4 backpackers can clean 80 cars in a day.

   a) Given that each backpacker cleans at the same rate, how many
      backpackers would it take to clean 140 cars in a day?

      .... ☐
      2 marks

   b) The backpackers get a new hose. 6 backpackers can now clean 144 cars
      in a day. How many days would it take 2 backpackers to clean 144 cars?

      .... ☐
      1 mark

Section Two — Review Exercise

5. A centipede travels 12 m in 40 seconds.

a) What is its average speed?

.... m/s □ 1 mark

b) The centipede changes its speed. It now scuttles along at 0.4 m/s.
How far will it travel in 17 seconds?

.... m □ 1 mark

6. A 520 g bar of gold has a volume of 27 cm³. What is the density of gold?
Give your answer to 1 decimal place and include the appropriate units.

.... □ 2 marks

7. Selma is making a banoffee pie.

a) She needs to buy some biscuits for the base. Two shops sell the biscuits she needs.

Bountiful Biscuits sells 400 g packs of biscuits for £1.22.
Cookie Crumbs sells 250 g packs of biscuits for 90p.

At which shop are the biscuits better value for money?

.... □ 2 marks

b) Selma uses a cake tin with a base area of 0.045 m².
Write the area in:

(i) cm²

.... cm²

(ii) mm²

.... mm² □ 2 marks

8. The town of Yolk lies 30 km north of Eggford.

a) Mark Yolk on the scale map on the right.

□ 1 mark

b) The village of Shell lies 5 miles west of Eggford.
How far apart would they be on this map?

1 mile ≈ 1.6 km

1 cm = 20 km

N

• Eggford

.... cm □ 2 marks

You're beginning to measure up to all the great mathematicians...

I think you deserve a congratulatory banoffee pie after all that (or whatever you can find in the kitchen). Proportion can be something that takes time to understand properly, so don't brush over any tricky topics. Once you know your stuff, you'll be able to find the best bargains in the next sales...

Score: □ / 25

Section Three — Algebra and Graphs

So... you've found my hoard of questions on Algebra and Graphs — I knew you would one day.
My next challenge for you is to find the answers (and I don't mean skipping to the answer page).

Before you Start

1.   **Expand the brackets in these expressions.**

     $5(p + 6) =$ .... $2(7 - q) =$ ....

2.   **Fully factorise these expressions.**

     $r - 15rs =$ .... $16t^2 - 8u =$ ....

3.   **Solve these equations.**

     a) $3(x + 6) = 4x$ b) $\dfrac{36 - 4y}{2} = 6$

     $x =$ .... $y =$ ....

4.   **Anita places an empty 5000 ml bucket under a leaky roof.**

     a)   Every hour, the amount (l ml) of water in the bucket increases by 20 ml.
          Write down a formula for l after h hours have passed.

          ....

     b)   How long does it take for the bucket to fill up?

          .... hours

5.   **Joshua writes down a sequence of numbers beginning: 17, 24, 31, 38, 45, ...**

     a)   Work out an expression for the nth term in the sequence.

          ....

     b)   Calculate the 20th term.   ....

6.   **Phoebe has found an ancient scroll showing a method to plot the graph of $y = 4x + 3$.**
     Follow the instructions on the scroll to plot the graph.

     Fill in this table of values for $y = 4x + 3$.

x	0	1	2	3
y				

     Plot the points from your table and
     connect them with a straight line.

     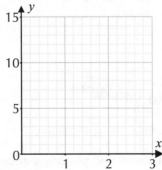

Expanding Brackets

1. Expand these brackets.

$-2(x + 1) =$ .... $x(x + 1) =$ .... $-x(2 - 3x) =$ ....

2. Expand these brackets by filling in the boxes and then collecting like terms.

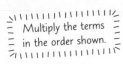 Multiply the terms in the order shown.

$(x + 1)(x + 2) =$ ☐ $+$ ☐ $+$ ☐ $+$ ☐ $=$ ....

3. Expand and simplify these double brackets.

Remember to simplify by collecting all the like terms.

a) $(w + 2)(w + 2)$

....

c) $(y + 1)(2y + 1)$

....

b) $(x + 3)(x + 6)$

....

d) $(z + 4)(z - 4)$

....

4. A rectangle has a width of $2x + 5$ and a height of $x - 2$, as shown below.

a) Write down an expression for the area of this rectangle using double brackets.

....

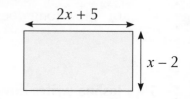

b) Expand and simplify the expression.

....

5. Expand and simplify these brackets.

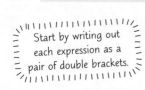 Start by writing out each expression as a pair of double brackets.

a) $(p + 3)^2$

....

b) $(q - 1)^2$

....

How did you do?

That was a lot of expanding — I feel like I'm about to burst. Now then, you need to be able to:

☐ Expand and simplify expressions containing double brackets.

Section Three — Algebra and Graphs

Factorising

1. Fill in the boxes to fully factorise these expressions.

$6w + 3wx = \boxed{} (2 + \boxed{})$ $\qquad$ $4y - 12yz = \boxed{} (1 - \boxed{})$

To fully factorise, you need to take out <u>all</u> of the common factors.

2. Fully factorise these expressions.

$14a + 7ab =$ .... $\qquad$ $15cd - 20c =$ ....

$-5e - 35ef =$ .... $\qquad$ $18g^2 - 2gh =$ ....

3. Chloe is having a tough time factorising.

Fill in the boxes to fully factorise this expression.

$27rs + 12rst + 15r^2 = \boxed{} (\boxed{} + 4st + \boxed{})$

4. Fully factorise these expressions.

$6x + 8xy + 10xz =$ .... $\qquad$ $5u + 25uv - 15u^2 =$ ....

5. Which numbers should replace the stars to give a correct factorisation?

Tick your answers ☑.

a) $x^2 + 4x + 3 = (x + 1)(x + \star)$ $\qquad$ ☐ 1 $\qquad$ ☐ 2 $\qquad$ ☐ 3

b) $x^2 + 6x + 5 = (x + \star)(x + 1)$ $\qquad$ ☐ 4 $\qquad$ ☐ 5 $\qquad$ ☐ 6

6. Factorise these expressions.

a) $x^2 + 3x + 2$ $\qquad\qquad\qquad$ b) $y^2 + 8y + 12$

.... $\qquad\qquad\qquad$ ....

How did you do?

Factorising is tricky, but with practice you'll get the hang of it. You can see if a factorisation is correct by expanding the brackets — you should get back to what you started with. Check you can:

☐ Factorise expressions using single brackets. $\qquad$ ☐ Factorise quadratics using double brackets.

 ☐ $\quad$ ☐ $\quad$ ☐

Solving Equations

1. Solve the following equations.

Expand any brackets first.

a) $13w + 9 = 6w + 30$

b) $21x + 1 = 4(9 + 4x)$

$w = \ldots\ldots$

$x = \ldots\ldots$

c) $2(3y - 2) = 6 + 7y$

d) $3(1 + 3z) = -2(5 - 4z)$

$y = \ldots\ldots$

$z = \ldots\ldots$

2. Solve these equations. Simplify your answers where possible.

a) $\dfrac{16}{3} = 2(u + 2)$

b) $5(1 - \dfrac{2}{5}v) = 7(2 - v)$

$u = \ldots\ldots$

$v = \ldots\ldots$

3. Mark was unable to solve the equations below on his computer. Show him how it's done and solve them by hand.

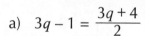

a) $3q - 1 = \dfrac{3q + 4}{2}$

b) $\dfrac{2(r + 1)}{5} = \dfrac{r + 3}{3}$

c) $t - 2 + \dfrac{t + 1}{4} = 12$

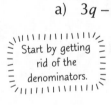
Start by getting rid of the denominators.

$q = \ldots\ldots$

$r = \ldots\ldots$

$t = \ldots\ldots$

How did you do?

Solving equations isn't guesswork — there's always a sequence of steps that get you to the solution. If you've found all the solutions on this page (and well done for that) you should be able to solve:

☐ Equations involving negatives.

☐ Equations involving fractions.

☐ Equations involving brackets.

☐ Equations with the unknown on both sides.

Section Three — Algebra and Graphs

Inequalities

1. Write down the inequality that represents each of the following statements.

n is less than 6 .... n is greater than or equal to 6 ....

2. Safia is thinking of a number, S. It is between 20 and 30, but not equal to either.

Which of these inequalities does S satisfy? Circle your answer.

$20 < S < 30$ $20 \leq S < 30$ $20 < S \leq 30$ $20 \leq S \leq 30$

3. List all the positive integer values of p that satisfy these inequalities.

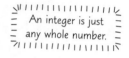
An integer is just any whole number.

$p \leq 4$ .... $p < 6$ ....

$2 < p \leq 5$ .... $1 \leq p \leq 3$ ....

4. The value of x is a whole number. Use the number line below to answer these questions.

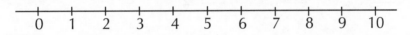

a) (i) Underline all values of x such that $x < 7$. (ii) Circle all values of x such that $x \geq 3$.

b) Write down an inequality for the values, x,
that are both underlined and circled. ....

5. Fill in the boxes with the correct inequality signs to represent the interval shown below.

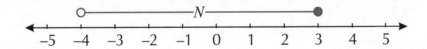

$-4\ \boxed{\phantom{<}}\ N\ \boxed{\phantom{<}}\ 3$

6. For each of the intervals shown, write down the equivalent inequality.

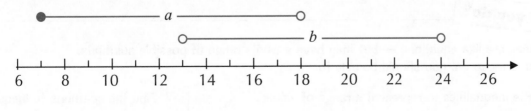

a: .... b: ....

Inequalities

7. Show each of these inequalities on the number lines provided.

a) (i) $-2 \leq x < 3$

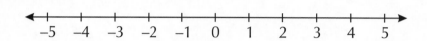

(ii) $-3 < x \leq 2$

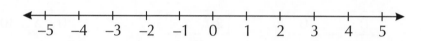

b) Write down an inequality for the values, x, that satisfy both of the inequalities from part a). ....

8. Joey is thinking of a number, y. It is positive and less than 10.

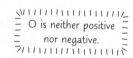

O is neither positive nor negative.

a) Write down an inequality to show the possible values of Joey's number. ....

b) Which of these could be Joey's number? Tick all possible answers.

☐ -2 ☐ 0 ☐ $\frac{1}{2}$ ☐ 9.99 ☐ 10

9. List all the positive integers, n, that satisfy the inequality $n + 2 < 7$.

....

10. Solve these inequalities.

a) $w + 1 \leq 5$ b) $6 - x > 5$

....

c) $-5 < y - 1$ d) $2z - 1 \geq 1$

....

How did you do?

Inequalities are like equations — but they have a whole range of possible solutions.
Before you move on, you should be able to:

☐ Write inequalities to represent a range of values.   ☐ Find the solutions to inequalities.

☐ Draw and interpret inequalities on number lines.

 ☐   ☐   ☐

Formulas

1. For each of these formulas, find the value of s when $u = 4$ and $t = -6$.

  a) $s = ut$

  b) $s = \dfrac{u - 2t}{4}$

  $s = $ ....

  $s = $ ....

2. Abigail is thinking of a number, N. She multiples it by 3, divides the result by 2 and then adds 1 to get M. Which of these is the correct formula to calculate M? Circle your answer.

$M = 3 \times \dfrac{N + 1}{2}$ $\qquad$ $M = \dfrac{3N}{2} + 1$ $\qquad$ $M = \dfrac{3N + 1}{2}$ $\qquad$ $M = \dfrac{N^3}{2} + 1$

3. Write down a formula for the area, A, of the shaded regions of these shapes.

A circle with radius r has an area of πr^2.

  a)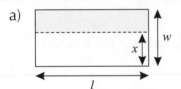

  b)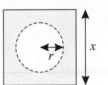

  $A = $ ....

  $A = $ ....

4. Morris's mobile plan charges £1.80 per gigabyte (GB) of data used.

  a) (i) Write down a formula for the cost C (in £) of using d GB of data.

  (ii) Use your formula to calculate the cost of using 25 GB of data.

  ....

  £ ....

  b) Morris changes to a plan that charges a flat fee of £10, plus 40p for every GB of data used. Write down a formula for the cost C (in £) of using d GB of data on this plan.

  ....

5. Rearrange the following formulas to make y the subject.

  a) $x = y + 5$ $\qquad$ $y = $ ....

  b) $x = 2y$ $\qquad$ $y = $ ....

  c) $x = \dfrac{y}{5}$ $\qquad$ $y = $ ....

  d) $x = 3y - 1$ $\qquad$ $y = $ ....

Section Three — Algebra and Graphs

Formulas

6. Rearrange the formulas below to make v the subject.

a) $u = 5 - 2v$

b) $u = 2vw$

....

....

c) $w = \dfrac{v - 1}{u}$

d) $v + u = w - v$

....

....

7. Misha has been told to mind her p's and q's. Help her out by answering this question.

a) Which of these is a correct rearrangement of $p = \sqrt{2q}$? Circle your answer.

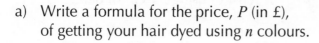

$$q = 2p^2 \qquad q = \tfrac{1}{2}p^2 \qquad q = \left(\tfrac{p}{2}\right)^2 \qquad q = (2p)^2$$

b) Rearrange the formula $p = 1 + q^3$ to make q the subject.

....

8. The surface area of a sphere, S, is given by the formula $S = 4\pi r^2$, where r is the radius.

a) Rearrange the formula to make r the subject.

$r = $ ....

b) What is the radius of a sphere that has a surface area of 36π cm²?

$r = $ .... cm

9. Sadie visits a hair salon to get her hair dyed. The stylist charges a fixed cost of £35, plus £4.50 for each colour used.

a) Write a formula for the price, P (in £), of getting your hair dyed using n colours.

....

b) (i) Rearrange your formula to make n the subject.

(ii) Sadie paid £62 to have her hair dyed. How many colours did the stylist use?

....

....

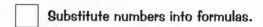

How did you do?

How many shades of blue can you name? I'm quite fond of "workbook blue" myself.
Now let's get some formalities out of the way — tick these boxes when you can:

☐ Write algebraic formulas from descriptions.

☐ Substitute numbers into formulas.

☐ Rearrange formulas to change their subject.

Sequences

1. Are these sequences arithmetic, geometric or neither? Underline your answer.

1, 3, 9, 27, 81, ...	Arithmetic	Geometric	Neither
5, 8, 11, 14, 17, ...	Arithmetic	Geometric	Neither
2, 5, 10, 17, 26, ...	Arithmetic	Geometric	Neither

2. A geometric sequence begins: 3, 6, 12, 24, 48, ...

What are the next three terms in this sequence? ...., ... and ....

3. A geometric sequence begins: 2, 6, N, 54, 162, ...

a) What is the value of N?   b) Circle each number below that is a term in the sequence.

N = ...

440	486	1440	1458	1486

4. A geometric sequence begins: 128, 64, 32, 16, 8, ...

Put a tick beside the ways you could end this sentence:
The sequence above will contain only...

☐ *... even numbers.*   ☐ *... positive numbers.*

☐ *... whole numbers.*   ☐ *... non-negative numbers.*

5. Write down the next three terms in each of these sequences.

a) $\frac{1}{2}$, $\frac{3}{2}$, $\frac{5}{2}$, $\frac{7}{2}$, $\frac{9}{2}$, ...

b) $\frac{1}{2}$, $\frac{2}{3}$, $\frac{3}{4}$, $\frac{4}{5}$, $\frac{5}{6}$, ...

.........., ..., ...

.........., ..., ...

6. A sequence begins: 1, 1, 2, 3, 5, 8, 13, 21, ...

What is the next term in the sequence?

What do you add to each term to get the next one?

....

How did you do?

This sequence of questions has come to an end. By now you should be able to:

☐ **Recognise and work with geometric sequences.**   ☐ **Spot patterns in unfamiliar sequences.**

 ☐   ☐   ☐

Finding the Equation of a Straight Line

1. Write down the gradient and *y*-intercept of the lines with the following equations.

a) $y = 2x + 1$

gradient = ..., *y*-intercept = ...

b) $y = 6 - 4x$

gradient = ..., *y*-intercept = ...

2. Write down the equation in the form $y = mx + c$ of the graph that has:

a) a gradient of 6 and a *y*-intercept of –5

....

b) a gradient of –7 and a *y*-intercept of 8

....

3. Calculate the gradient of the line segment between these pairs of points.

a) (5, 1) and (6, 4)

b) (–2, 8) and (0, 6)

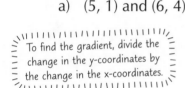
To find the gradient, divide the change in the y-coordinates by the change in the x-coordinates.

....

....

4. Val has drawn a line on the axes on the right.

a) Calculate the gradient of Val's line.

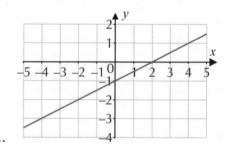

....

b) Tick the equation of each line that is parallel to Val's line.

☐ $y = 2x + 1$ ☐ $y = \frac{1}{2}x + 1$ ☐ $y = x - \frac{1}{2}$ ☐ $y = \frac{1}{2}x$

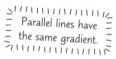
Parallel lines have the same gradient.

5. Rearrange these equations into the form $y = mx + c$ and then write down the gradient and the coordinates of the *y*-intercept.

Equation	$y = mx + c$ form	Gradient	Coordinates of *y*-intercept
$-5 = y - 6x$	....	....	(........., ...)
$2y - 4x = 6$	....	....	(........., ...)
$\frac{y}{2} + 2x = 3$	....	....	(........., ...)

Section Three — Algebra and Graphs

Finding the Equation of a Straight Line

6. A line passes through the points (0, 3) and (2, 13). What is the equation of this line?

Circle your answer.

| $y = -3x + 5$ | $y = 5x - 3$ | $y = -5x + 3$ | $y = 5x + 3$ | $y = 3x + 5$ |

7. Find the equations of the lines drawn on these axes.

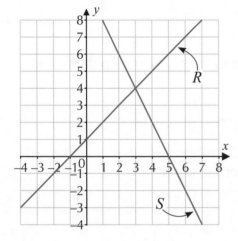

Give your answers in the form $y = mx + c$.

a) Line R

....

b) Line S

....

8. Robbie has drawn a line, L, and plotted a point, P, on the axes below.

a) Find the gradient of L.

....

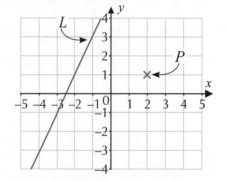

b) (i) Use your answer to part a) to find the equation of the line parallel to L that passes through P.

....

(ii) Sketch the line on the axes.

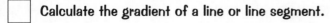

How did you do?

There's a fine line between an empty set of axes and a correctly plotted graph. If you've completed all these questions, you should now be able to:

- ☐ Calculate the gradient of a line or line segment.
- ☐ Write the equation of a line in the form $y = mx + c$.
- ☐ Find the equation of a line.

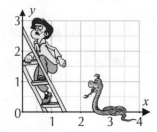

 ☐   ☐   ☐

Section Three — Algebra and Graphs

Quadratic Graphs

1. Consider the quadratic equation $y = x^2 + 1$.

   a) Complete this table of values for the equation.

x	–4	–2	0	2	4
x^2	....	....	....	....	....
$y = x^2 + 1$	....	....	....	....	....

   b) (i) Plot each pair of x- and y-values from your table as coordinates on the axes on the right.

      (ii) Sketch the graph of $y = x^2 + 1$ by drawing a smooth curve joining up the points.

2. Noel has plotted the graph of the equation $y = x^2 - 5$ on the axes below.

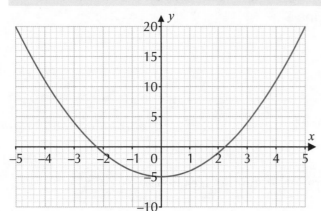

   a) (i) Complete this table of values for the equation $y = x^2 - 9$.

x	–5	–3	0	3	5
x^2	....	....	....	9	25
$x^2 - 9$	....	....	....	0	16

      (ii) Use your table to plot the graph of the equation $y = x^2 - 9$ on the same axes.

   b) (i) What are the coordinates of the y-intercept of Noel's graph? (........, ...)

      (ii) What feature of your graph is related to the '– 9' in the equation $y = x^2 - 9$?

      ....

      (iii) Where does the graph of the equation $y = x^2 + x + 2$ cross the y-axis? (........, ...)

   c) Does the graph of $y = x^2 - 9$ ever intersect Noel's graph? Explain your answer.

   ....

   ....

3. Gail has sketched a graph on the right.

Which of these equations could represent Gail's graph? Tick your answer.

     $y = x^2 + 3$ ☐ $y = -x^2 + 3$ ☐

     $y = x^2 - 3$ ☐ $y = -x^2 - 3$ ☐

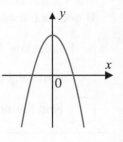

Quadratic Graphs

4. Consider the quadratic equation $y = x^2 - 6x + 9$.

a) Complete this table of values for the equation.

x	0	1	2	3	4	5
y	9	4	....	....	....	....

b) Use your table of values to plot the graph of $y = x^2 - 6x + 9$ for values of x from 0 to 5.

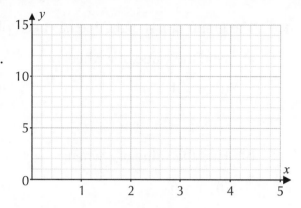

5. Imran has sketched the graphs of four quadratic equations below.

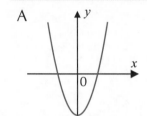 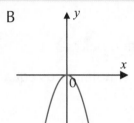 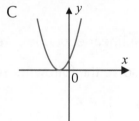 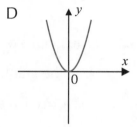

Write A, B, C or D in the boxes below to match each graph with its equation.

$y = x^2$ ☐ $y = -x^2$ ☐ $y = x^2 - 2$ ☐ $y = x^2 + 2x + 1$ ☐

6. Consider the equation $y = -x^2 + 3x - 2$.

a) Complete this table of values for the equation.

x	0	1	1.5	2	3
y	....	....	....	....	....

b) Use your table to sketch a graph of the equation on the axes on the right.

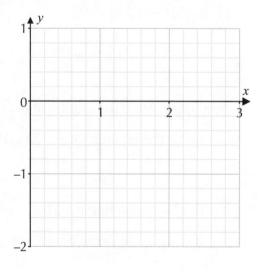

Section Three — Algebra and Graphs

Solving Equations Using Graphs

1. The graph of a straight line has been plotted on the right.

   a) Find the value of y when:

      (i) $x = 1$ (ii) $x = 3$

              $y = $ .... $y = $ ....

   b) Find the value of x when:

      (i) $y = 5$ (ii) $y = 55$

              $x = $ .... $x = $ ....

      (iii) $y = 25$ (iv) $y = 65$

              $x = $ .... $x = $ ....

2. The graphs of three linear equations are plotted below.

   The solutions are where the lines meet.

   Use the graphs to solve the following sets of simultaneous equations.

   a) $y = x + 6$ and $y = 3x + 4$

              $x = $ ...., $y = $ ....

   b) $y = x + 6$ and $y = 2 - x$

              $x = $ ...., $y = $ ....

   c) $y = 3x + 4$ and $y = 2 - x$

              $x = $ ...., $y = $ ....

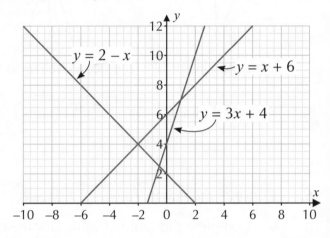

3. Amy has plotted the graphs of $y = 4x^2 - 8x - 12$ and $y = 4x + 4$.

   a) Solve the equation $4x^2 - 8x - 12 = 0$.

              $x = $ .... or $x = $ ....

   b) (i) Draw the line $y = 20$.

      (ii) Solve the equation $4x^2 - 8x - 12 = 20$.

              $x = $ .... or $x = $ ....

   c) Solve the simultaneous equations
      $y = 4x^2 - 8x - 12$ and $y = 4x + 4$.

              $x = $ ...., $y = $ ....

              $x = $ ...., $y = $ ....

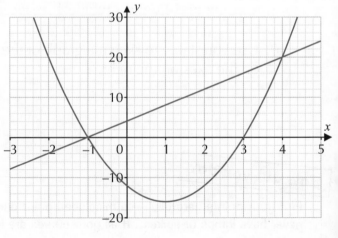

Solving Equations Using Graphs

4. The graph of the cubic equation $y = x^3 - 3x^2 - x + 5$ is shown below.

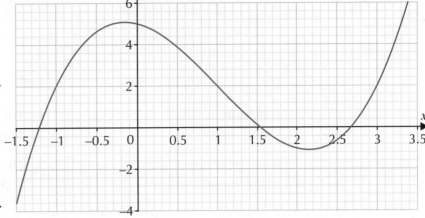

A cubic equation has x^3 as its highest power.

a) Find three solutions to the equation $x^3 - 3x^2 - x + 5 = 2$.

$x = \ldots\ldots\ldots, \ldots\ldots\ldots, \ldots\ldots\ldots$

b) Estimate a solution to the equation $x^3 - 3x^2 - x + 5 = -2$.

$x = \ldots\ldots\ldots$

5. The graph of $y = 2^x$ is shown on the right.

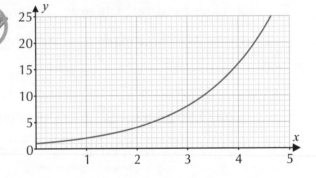

a) Find the value of x for these values of y.

(i) $y = 2$

$x = \ldots\ldots\ldots$

(ii) $y = 16$

$x = \ldots\ldots\ldots$

b) (i) Find the solution to the equation $2^x = 4$.

$x = \ldots\ldots\ldots$

(ii) Estimate the solution to the equation $2^x = 17$.

$x = \ldots\ldots\ldots$

6. The graph of $y = \dfrac{A}{x}$ is shown on the right.

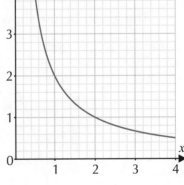

a) What is the value of y when $x = 2$?

$y = \ldots\ldots\ldots$

b) Use your answer to part a) to calculate the value of A.

$A = \ldots\ldots\ldots$

c) Draw the line $y = x$ and use it to estimate the solution to the simultaneous equations $y = \dfrac{A}{x}$ and $y = x$.

$x = \ldots\ldots\ldots, \quad y = \ldots\ldots\ldots$

How did you do?

Go on then, I'll allow a *small* range of answers to your approximation solutions. You should be able to:

☐ Use graphs to find or estimate solutions to equations.

☐ Solve simultaneous equations using the graphs of the equations.

 ☐ ☐ ☐

Real-Life Graphs

1. Match the graphs below with the real-life situations that they could model.

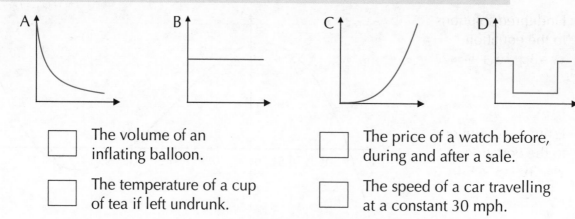

☐ The volume of an inflating balloon.

☐ The price of a watch before, during and after a sale.

☐ The temperature of a cup of tea if left undrunk.

☐ The speed of a car travelling at a constant 30 mph.

2. John jogs to work 2 km away. The graph below shows how far he travels over time.

a) (i) After how many minutes did John's speed change?

.... minutes

(ii) Did John speed up or slow down at this time?

☐ He sped up   ☐ He slowed down

b) If instead John had continued at his original pace, how long would it have taken him to get to work?

.... minutes

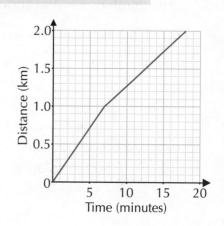

3. Stephanie hits a tennis ball into the air and watches it bounce.

The graph below shows the height of the tennis ball above the ground over time.

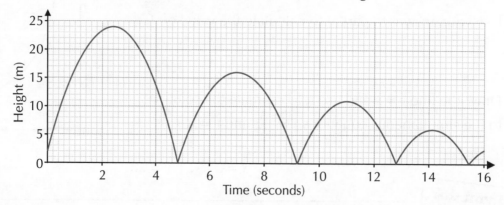

a) What was the greatest height that the tennis ball reached?   .... m

b) (i) Mark an X on the graph each time the ball hits the ground.

(ii) How much time passed between the first time the ball hit the ground and the second time?   .... s

Real-Life Graphs

4. The graph shows possible lengths for the base, b, and height, h, of a triangle with a fixed area, A.

a) (i) Estimate the height when the base is 2 cm. .... cm

(ii) Estimate the base when the height is 4.2 cm. .... cm

b) What is the area of the triangle?

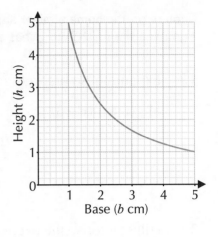

A = ... cm^2

5. Kieran makes candles by pouring melted wax into the jars on the right.

Each jar has the same height and volume.

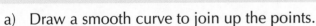

The graph on the left shows how the depth of the wax in the jars changes with the amount of wax used.

a) 200 g of wax is poured into each of jars 1 and 2. Which will have the greatest depth of wax?

Jar ....

b) On the same axes, sketch the graph for jar 3.

6. A model car is pushed off a cliff. Its height is recorded as it falls and plotted on the right.

a) Draw a smooth curve to join up the points.

b) Using your curve, estimate the height of the car after:

(i) 1 second .... m

(ii) 1.6 seconds .... m

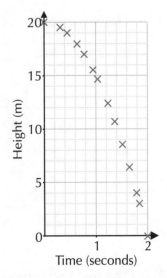

c) Which of these formulas best describes the height, h, of the car, t seconds after it leaves the cliff edge? Circle your answer.

$h = 20 + 5t^2$ $\quad$ $h = 20 - 5t^2$ $\quad$ $h = -5t^2 - 20$

How did you do?

You can find all sorts of graphs cropping up in real-life situations. You need to make sure you can:

☐ Draw real-life graphs. $\qquad$ ☐ Read off and interpret real-life graphs.

Section Three — Algebra and Graphs

Section Three — Review Exercise

You're on the home straight and there's only these review questions left between you and the finish line. What are you waiting for? Go and take them in your stride.

1. Expand these brackets and collect like terms.

   a) $(x + 5)(x + 3)$

   b) $(p + 7)(2 - p)$

   ....

   2 marks

2. Fully factorise the expression $12ab - 6b + 15bc$.

   ....

   1 mark

3. Becky and Bilal buy packets of water balloons. A single packet contains n balloons. Becky buys 6 packets and throws 8 balloons at Bilal.

   a) Write an expression for the number of balloons Becky has left over.

   ....

   1 mark

   b) The number of balloons Bilal has is represented by $\frac{7n - 1}{2}$. If they each have the same number of balloons left, how many balloons are in each packet?

   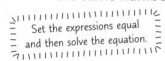
   Set the expressions equal and then solve the equation.

   ....

   2 marks

4. Draw the solution to these inequalities on the number lines below.

   a) $x - 3 < -1$

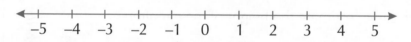

   b) $2y - 1 \geq y$

   1 mark

   1 mark

5. The first two terms of a sequence are 4 and 12. Write down the next two terms if the sequence is:

   a) arithmetic

   ...., ...

   b) geometric

   ...., ...

   4 marks

Section Three — Review Exercise

6. Erin starts the month with £63. Each day Erin spends £3.50 on lunch.

a) Write down a formula for the amount of money, £M, that Erin has after d days.

....

b) (i) Rearrange the formula to make d the subject.

....

(ii) After how many days will Erin run out of money?

.... days

7. Magnus has sketched the graphs of two straight lines below.

a) Work out the equation of line L in the form $y = mx + c$.

....

b) (i) Use the table of values below to plot the graph of $y = 6x^2 - 20x + 18$ on the same axes.

x	0	1	2	3	4
y	18	4	2	12	34

(ii) Use the graphs to find two solutions to the equation $4x = 6x^2 - 20x + 18$.

$x = $ .... and $x = $ ....

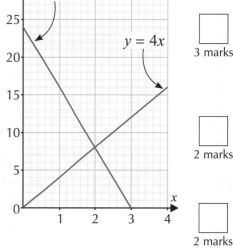

8. The graph shows the charge left in the battery in Owen's mobile phone.

a) How long did it take for the battery to first reach 50% charge?

.... hours

b) After a time, the phone was plugged in and left to charge. By how much did the charge increase during this time?

.... %

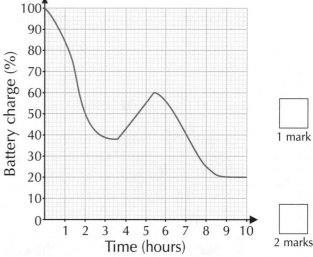

I'm feeling positively charged after all those problems...

What's that? You've finished already? Fantastic stuff. Go ahead and mark your answers. We've all got different strengths and weaknesses, so you'll have to do a bit of self-reflection to decide what needs going over. Don't let the context of a real-life problem faze you — it's all about the numbers.

Score:
27

Section Four — Geometry

Section Four already? Wow, this book is practically completing itself... What do you mean, 'It's not'?
Don't complain too loudly yet — you've got a whole section on geometry coming up. But first:

Before you Start

1. **Circle the shapes that are congruent.**

   'Congruent' means
   same shape, same size.

     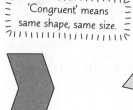

2. **Find the lettered angles.**

   a)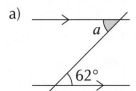

   b)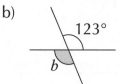

   c)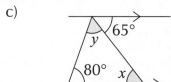

   $a =$ ....° $b =$ ....° $x =$ ....° $y =$ ....°

3. **A manhole cover has a diameter of 80 cm.**

   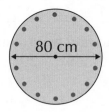

   a) Work out the circumference
       of the manhole cover to 3 s.f.

   .... cm

   b) What is the area of the manhole cover? Give your answer to 3 s.f.

   .... cm²

4. **Look at the cuboid below.**

   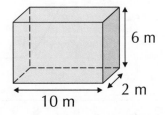

   6 m

   2 m

   10 m

   a) Sketch and label a net of the cuboid in the space above.

   b) Work out the volume of the cuboid.

   $V =$ .... m³

Polygons

1. Sort the letters of the shapes into the table on the right.

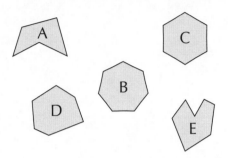

Shape	Regular	Irregular
Pentagon		
Hexagon		
Heptagon		

2. The diagram shows a ramp in a skate park.
   It makes an angle r with the ground. Find r.

   The diagram is not drawn accurately.

   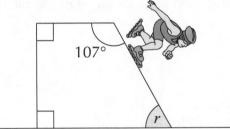

   $107°$

   r

   $r =$ .... °

3. A pentagon can be split up into 3 triangles, as shown on the right.

   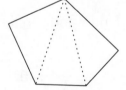

   a) Fill in the blanks to complete the working below.

   > The interior angles in one triangle add up to .... °,
   >
   > so the interior angles in a pentagon add up to .... × .... ° = ... ° .

   b) Adebayo splits an octagon into triangles in the same way.

      (i) How many triangles are in an octagon?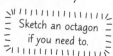

      Sketch an octagon if you need to.

      ....

      (ii) What is the sum of the interior angles in an octagon?

      .... °

Polygons

4. Hexagon Rock is a regular hexagon and a popular diving spot by Lake Splashmere.

Find the angles p and q.

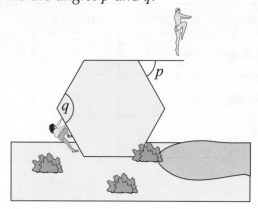

$p =$ .... °

$q =$ .... °

5. Afia has baked a pie in the shape of a regular decagon.

Work out the size of each interior and exterior angle of the pie.

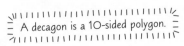
A decagon is a 10-sided polygon.

Exterior angle: .... °   Interior angle: .... °

6. Find x and y in the irregular polygon below.

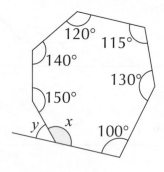

120°   115°

140°

130°

150°

y x 100°

$x =$ .... °

$y =$ .... °

How did you do?

Freshly baked pie, anyone? Once you've finished these pages, make sure you can:

☐ Find the sum of the interior angles in a polygon.

☐ Find interior and exterior angles in regular polygons.

☐ Use the sum of the interior and exterior angles to find unknown angles in irregular polygons.

 ☐   ☐   ☐

Loci and Constructions

1. Use compasses and a ruler to draw a perpendicular bisector of the line *AB*.

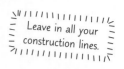
Leave in all your construction lines.

A •————————————• B

2. Sam the snowman wants to hide from the midday sun. He finds shade under a tree, but soon realises he can't go further than 2 m from the tree before he starts to melt.

Using compasses and the scale 2 cm = 1 m, shade the area on the diagram below that Sam can safely stand in.

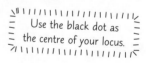
Use the black dot as the centre of your locus.

Loci and Constructions

3. Use compasses and a ruler to bisect angle *DEF*.

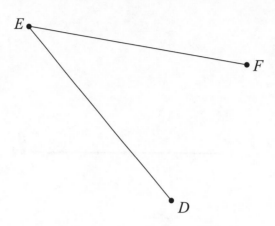

4. Thor stands at point *T* and throws his hammer through wall *AB*.
The hammer takes the shortest path from Thor to the wall.

Use compasses and a ruler to draw the path that the hammer takes.

T

A   *B*

How did you do?

Oh no, the hammer's coming back our way... duuuck! *Woooosh* Phew, I think we're okay...
While you recover from that dramatic incident, check that you can use a ruler and compasses to:

☐ Construct a perpendicular bisector of a line segment.

☐ Draw simple loci around points and lines.

☐ Bisect the angle between two line segments.

☐ Construct a perpendicular line to a given line through or from a given point.

Transformations

1. Each shape below has been enlarged from a centre of enlargement marked by a dot. The shapes with the dashed lines represent the enlarged shape.

Draw lines to match each enlargement with the correct scale factor.

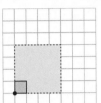   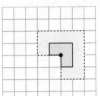   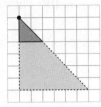

Scale factor 2   Scale factor 3   Scale factor 4

2. Write down the vector for the translations of:

a) M to N

....

b) N to M

....

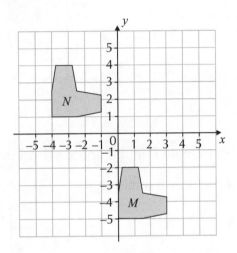

3. Look at the grid on the right.

a) Square V is a reflection of square T. What is the equation of the mirror line for this reflection?

....

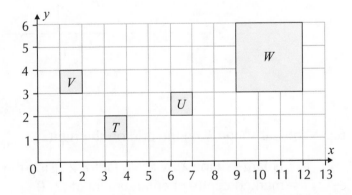

b) Describe the rotation that would map square V onto square U. The coordinates of the centre of rotation are whole numbers.

....

c) Describe the enlargement that would map square T onto square W.

....

Section Four — Geometry

Transformations

4. Amaya and Marshall are having a picnic on a chequered blanket when a trail of ants invades.

   The ants move a box of cherries (C) so that, relative to the origin,

   it is translated by the vector $\begin{pmatrix} 4 \\ -1 \end{pmatrix}$, and then by the vector $\begin{pmatrix} -2 \\ 4 \end{pmatrix}$.

   Draw the new position of the box on the grid below. Label it D.

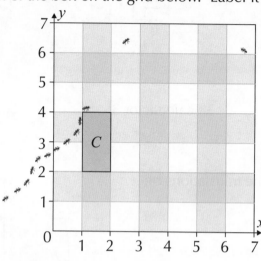

5. Reflect triangle P in the line x = 2 on the grid below.

   Label the new triangle Q.

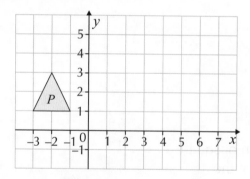

6. Look at shape X on the grid on the right.

   a) Enlarge shape X by scale factor 2 using the marked centre of enlargement at (2, 0). Label the new shape Y.

   b) Translate shape X by the vector $\begin{pmatrix} -1 \\ 3 \end{pmatrix}$. Label the new shape Z.

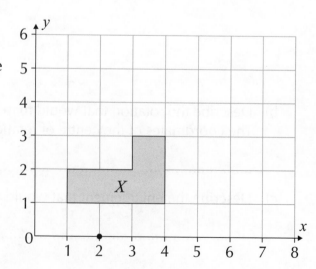

Transformations

7. The ear of the elephant below has been drawn on this grid.

Enlarge the elephant's ear, *E*, on the grid by scale factor 3 and with centre of enlargement (7, 6). Label the enlarged ear *F*.

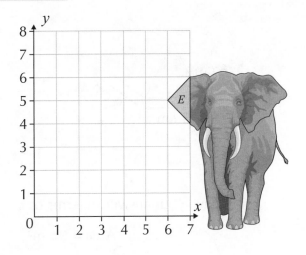

8. Dr. Eve L. Genius is sitting in her office on her chair, *B*.

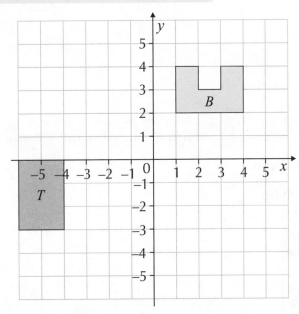

a) Dr. Genius rotates her chair 90° clockwise about the origin. Draw the chair after the rotation. Label it *C*.

b) She then pushes the rotated chair, *C*, so that it is translated by the vector $\begin{pmatrix} -7 \\ -1 \end{pmatrix}$. Does she collide with the table, *T*? Circle your answer.

Yes / No

3D Shapes

1. Find the volume of the following prisms and cylinders. Give the correct units.

a)

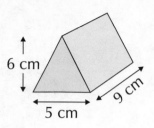

6 cm

5 cm

9 cm

....

b)

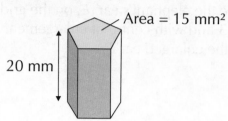

Area = 15 mm²

20 mm

....

c) Leave your answer in terms of π.

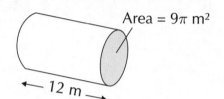

Area = 9π m²

12 m

....

d) Leave your answer in terms of π.

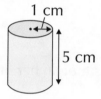

1 cm

5 cm

....

2. Monica bought a cylindrical tub of fish food. Work out the volume of the tub.

Give your answer to 1 d.p.

6 cm

20 cm

Fish food

.... cm³

3. A cylindrical tank of treacle has a volume of 72π m³ and a cross-sectional area of 6π m².

What is the height, h, of the tank?

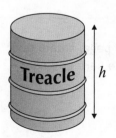

Treacle h

.... m

3D Shapes

4. A square-based pyramid has a base area of 4 cm².
Each triangular face is isosceles and has a height of 2 cm.

Use a ruler to draw an accurate net of the pyramid on the grid below.

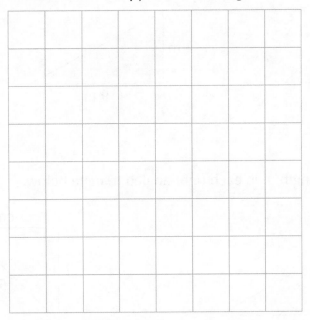

5. The shape below is made up of a cuboid and a cylinder. Find its volume to 1 d.p.

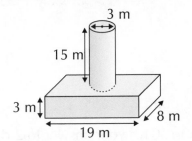

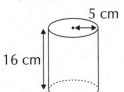

.... m³

6. Find the area of the net of the cylinder below.

Give your answer to 1 d.p.

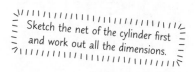

Sketch the net of the cylinder first and work out all the dimensions.

.... cm²

How did you do?

While I'm busy sketching Annette, check you can:

☐ Draw nets of 3D shapes and use them to solve problems.

☐ Find the volumes of prisms, including cylinders.

 ☐   ☐   ☐

Section Four — Geometry

Pythagoras' Theorem

1. Circle the triangle with a hypotenuse of 10 m.

None of the diagrams on this page are drawn accurately.

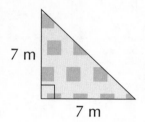

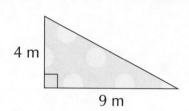

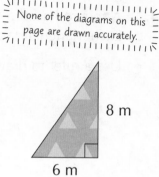

2. Find the missing length, *l*, in each right-angled triangle below.

a)

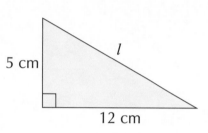

l = ... cm

b)

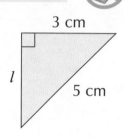

l = ... cm

3. Bailey's front door is 0.4 m above the horizontal ground.
Bailey uses a 6 m long ramp to get from the front door to the ground.

How far does the ramp extend horizontally from the front door? Give your answer to 2 d.p.

Sketch a diagram of the ramp first to help you.

.... m

How did you do?

When Pythagoras was playing around with this theorem way back in the 6th century BC, I wonder if he knew it'd be the best thing about school* for so many teenagers one day... See if you can now:

☐ Use Pythagoras' theorem to find any missing side length of a right-angled triangle.

*based on my own experience

Section Four — Geometry

Trigonometry

1. Use trigonometry to calculate the lettered angle in each triangle.

Give your answers to 1 d.p.

a)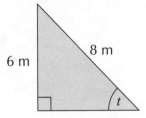

b)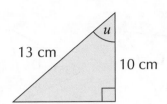

c)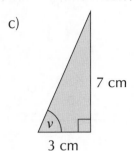

$t = \dots\dots\dots°$

$u = \dots\dots\dots°$

$v = \dots\dots\dots°$

2. Calculate the length *DE* in each triangle below.

Give your answers to 1 d.p.

a)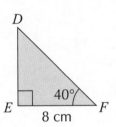

b)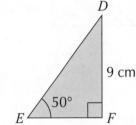

$DE = \dots\dots\dots$ cm

$DE = \dots\dots\dots$ cm

3. A cyclist approaches a hill and sees the sign on the right.
It means that for every 3 m horizontally, the hill rises by 1 m vertically.

Find the angle that the hill makes with the horizontal to 1 d.p.

WARNING
STEEP GRADIENT
AHEAD
1:3

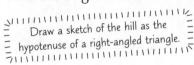
Draw a sketch of the hill as the hypotenuse of a right-angled triangle.

$\dots\dots\dots°$

How did you do?

Trigo-YES-metry, more like... (Sorry, I should have *angled* that pun a little better.)
When you've finished the page, make sure you can use trigonometry to:

☐ Find angles in right-angled triangles.   ☐ Find side lengths of right-angled triangles.

 ☐   ☐   ☐

Similarity and Congruence

1. Circle all the triangles that are definitely congruent to A.

   The triangles are not drawn to scale.

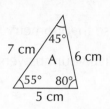

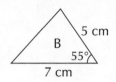 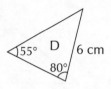 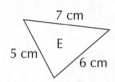

2. The two triangles below are similar.

   Fill in the missing labels.

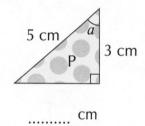 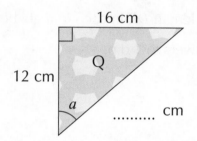

3. The two trapeziums below are similar.

   Fill in the missing labels.

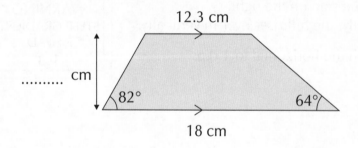 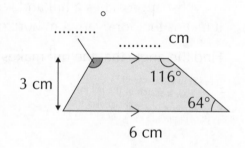

How did you do?

Similarity and congruence can easily get mixed up. Remember, 'similar siblings, congruent clones' — congruent shapes are exactly the same, but similar shapes generally aren't. Now check you can:

☐ Identify congruent triangles using the criteria for congruence.

☐ Label the sides and angles of similar triangles and other similar shapes.

Section Four — Geometry

Geometric Relationships

1. Look at the diagram below.

XYZ is a triangle. *UXV* and *TYZW* are parallel lines.

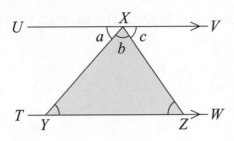

a) What is the sum of the angles *a*, *b* and *c*?

.............°

b) Use the triangle above and your knowledge about angles around parallel lines to prove that the angles within any triangle add up to 180°.

....

....

....

2. The diagram below shows the triangle *PQR*.

SPR is a straight line.

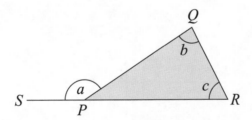

Prove that *a* = *b* + *c*.

....

....

....

....

How did you do?

A geometric relationship? Sounds like it'd make for a boring rom-com...
Before you move on from these relationships, check that you can:

☐ Use facts about lines, angles and shapes to prove other geometric relationships.

Section Four — Review Exercise

Another Review Exercise for you — I'm too kind. Before you get going, go back over the section to see if there's anything you need to revisit. Then get cracking on this and see how you do.

1. Find s and t in the regular pentagon below. The diagram is not drawn accurately.

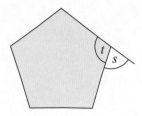

$s = \ldots\ldots\ldots\ldots^{\circ}$

$t = \ldots\ldots\ldots\ldots^{\circ}$

3 marks

2. Draw a line perpendicular to AB through point P.
Use compasses and a ruler.

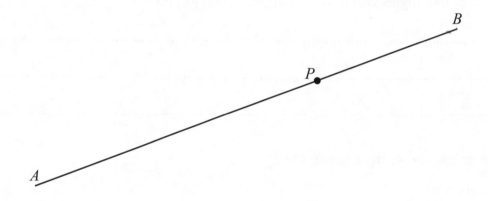

2 marks

3. Look at the grid below.

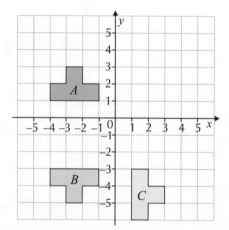

a) Describe the transformation that maps shape A onto shape B.

....

2 marks

b) Describe the transformation that maps shape B onto shape C.

....

3 marks

Section Four — Review Exercise

4. Work out the volume of the can of hairspray. Give your answer to 1 d.p.
The can is not drawn to scale.

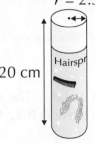

$r = 2.5$ cm

20 cm

$V = $ .... cm³ ☐

2 marks

5. Find the missing lengths in the triangles below, giving your answers to 1 d.p.
The triangles are not drawn accurately.

a)

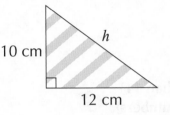

10 cm

h

12 cm

b)

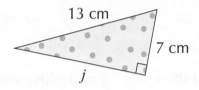

13 cm

7 cm

j

$h = $ .... cm $j = $ .... cm ☐

4 marks

6. Look at the triangles below. Neither triangle is drawn accurately.

a) Find angle x to 1 d.p.

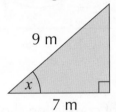

9 m

x

7 m

b) Find length BC to 1 d.p.

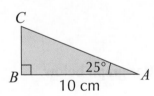

C

B 25° A

10 cm

$x = $ .... ° $BC = $ .... cm ☐

4 marks

7. Triangle Z below is similar to triangle Y.
Fill in the missing labels. Neither triangle is drawn accurately.

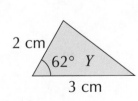

2 cm

62° Y

3 cm

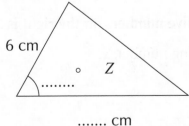

6 cm

Z

....

.... cm

2 marks

Hopefully you won't need hairspray to keep up this good work...

Yay — that's another section done. Time to take a break and go get yourself some biscuits, I think.
Then come back and mark this last couple of pages. There are quite a few topics that may be new
here, so take some time to go over anything you think might need a little more work.

Score:

22

Section Five — Probability and Statistics

Statistically speaking, this is the section that people look forward to the most. 9.9 out of 10 people said they'd probably recommend it to a friend. Try these warm-up questions first, then see if you agree.

Before you Start

1. **A plane can land either early, on time or late. The probability that it lands late is 0.4 and the probability that it lands early is 0.1. What is the probability that:**

   a) the plane does not land early?

   ....

   b) the plane lands on time?

   ....

2. **Look at these sets:** ξ = {positive whole numbers less than 11}
   A = {factors of 100}   B = {odd numbers}

   a) Write down all the members of A.

   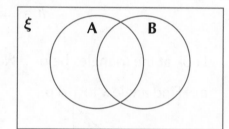

   ....

   b) Put all the elements of ξ in the correct place on the Venn diagram.

3. **Look at the scatter graph below.**

   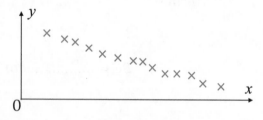

   a) Circle the type of correlation shown.

      Positive   Negative   None

   b) Draw a line of best fit on the graph.

4. **The mean of the five numbers on the right is 5.**   8 1 2 x 6

   a) Find the missing number, x.

      x = ...

   b) A sixth number, 9, is added. What is the median of the six numbers?

      ....

Probability from Experiments

1. The spinner below is spun 60 times. The table shows the results.

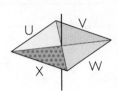

	U	V	W	X
Frequency	6	18	21	15
Relative frequency	....	....	....	....

> To find the relative frequency of an event, divide its frequency by the number of times the 'experiment' was carried out.

a) Complete the table, giving the values as decimals.

b) Do you think the spinner is fair or biased? Explain your answer.

....

....

2. Felicity tosses a biased coin 600 times. How many times would you expect the coin to land on heads if the probability of it landing on heads is...

a) $\frac{1}{3}$?

b) $\frac{2}{5}$?

c) 1?

....

3. A game at a carnival guarantees that everyone who plays wins one of the prizes on the right. 40 people play the game.

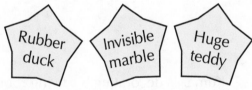

a) 22 people win a rubber duck.
What is the relative frequency of winning a rubber duck?

....

b) The relative frequency of winning an invisible marble is 0.35.
How many people have won an invisible marble?

....

c) Work out an estimate for the probability of winning a huge teddy.

....

How did you do?

I expect that you probably found this page a blast. But then I would say that — I'm pretty biased in favour of this kind of thing. Now then, before moving on make sure you know how to:

☐ Find relative frequencies and use these to estimate probabilities.

☐ Work out expected frequencies.   ☐ Decide if an experiment is fair or biased.

 ☐   ☐   ☐

Section Five — Probability and Statistics

Theoretical Probability

1. The table on the right shows some information about the sandwiches at a party.

	Vegetarian	Meaty
Gluten-free	6	3
Contains gluten	9	7

Chester picks a sandwich to eat at random.
Giving your answers as fractions in their simplest form, find the probability that he picks a sandwich that is:

Start by finding the total number of sandwiches.

a) gluten-free and vegetarian

....

b) meaty

....

2. Chris rolls a fair 12-sided dice, labelled 1 to 12.

a) The probability of rolling a 3 or lower is 0.25. Chris claims that this means the probability of rolling a 3 or higher is 1 – 0.25 = 0.75. Explain why Chris is wrong.

....

....

b) Chris now rolls a different 12-sided dice. There is an equal chance of it landing on any particular face. The probability of rolling a 7 is $\frac{1}{3}$. How many faces of the dice are labelled with a 7?

....

3. Kumar is decorating his living room. He can paint the walls either black or cream. He can cover the floor in wood, carpet or marzipan.

a) List all the possible ways that he can decorate his living room. Two have been done for you.

Black walls with wood floor   Cream walls with wood floor

b) Kumar decides to choose how to decorate his living room at random. His choice for the walls does not affect his choice for the floors. Giving each answer as a fraction in its simplest form, work out:

(i) the probability that he paints the walls black and covers the floor in carpet.

....

(ii) the probability that he paints the walls cream or covers the floor in marzipan, or both.

....

Theoretical Probability

4. There are 50 elephants in a herd.
The Venn diagram on the right shows
how many of them can fly and how
many of them can play the piano.

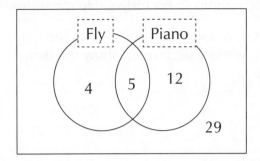

a) (i) How many of the elephants can
neither fly nor play the piano?

....

(ii) Shade the part of the Venn diagram that shows the number
of elephants that can play the piano but can't fly.

b) An elephant is chosen at random from the herd.
What is the probability, as a decimal, that the elephant...

(i) can fly?   (ii) can both fly and play the piano?

....

5. A bag contains 40 cards. Each card is labelled with a different number from 1 to 40.
Betty picks a card at random from the bag, notes down whether the number is a multiple
of 10, then puts it back. She then picks out another card at random and does the same.

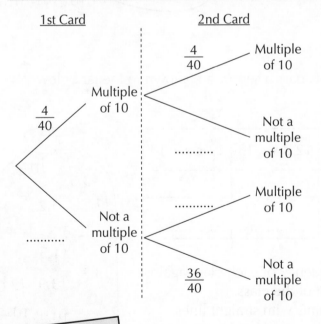

The diagram on the left
is a tree diagram.

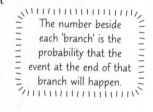

The number beside
each 'branch' is the
probability that the
event at the end of that
branch will happen.

a) Complete the tree
diagram by filling
in the missing
probabilities.

b) Suppose that Betty picks a card that
shows a multiple of 10, and then
doesn't put the card back into the bag.

What is the probability that the
second card Betty picks is also a
multiple of 10?

....

How did you do?

Well, probability — it's been swell. But life keeps rolling forward and the time has come to move along
to the next topic. Before heading off, have a quick think and make absolutely sure that you can:

[ ] Calculate theoretical probabilities.

[ ] Use Venn diagrams, sample spaces and tree diagrams to organise information and find probabilities.

Displaying Data

1. Jim has 10 cartons in his fridge. He measures the amount of liquid left in each one.

The results are shown in the table on the right.
Draw a frequency diagram to show the data.

Liquid left (v ml)	Frequency
$0 < v \le 200$	2
$200 < v \le 400$	4
$400 < v \le 600$	3
$600 < v \le 800$	1

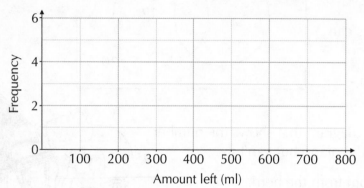

There shouldn't be any gaps between the bars since there aren't any gaps between the classes.

2. The values below are the lengths of the antlers of several deer (in centimetres).

35   26   27   41   46   45   49   48   28

Construct an ordered stem and leaf diagram to display the data.
Some values have been filled in for you.

```
2 | 6  7
3 |
4 |
```

Key: 2 | 6 = 26 cm

The 'stem' is the tens value (2, 3 or 4).
The 'leaf' is the units value.

3. The speeds, s mph, at which several cyclists pass a sensor are shown in the jar below.

   a) Complete this grouped frequency table.

Speed (s mph)	$10 \le s < 11$	$11 \le s < 12$	$12 \le s < 13$	$13 \le s < 14$
Tally				
Frequency	....	....	....	....

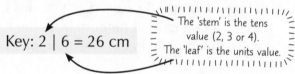

   b) On the axes below: (i) Plot the frequency of each class against the midpoint of the class.
   (ii) Join your points with straight lines.

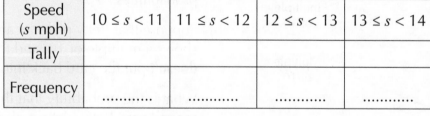

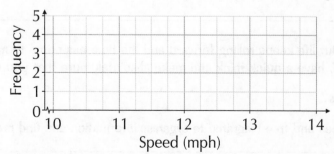

The diagram you've drawn in part b) is called a frequency polygon. You can have a go at interpreting one in Question 4.

Section Five — Probability and Statistics

Displaying Data

4. The diagram below is a frequency polygon showing the masses of all the horses in a stable.

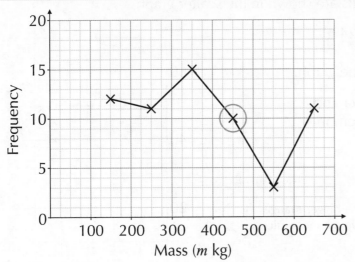

Mass (*m* kg)

The circled point is for the class 400 kg < *m* ≤ 500 kg. The frequency of this class is 10. All the classes have the same width.

a) How many horses had a mass of between 100 kg and 200 kg?

....

b) How many horses had a mass greater than 400 kg?

....

c) Write down the modal class.

....

5. Some data is collected about a group of authors.

```
0 | 1  2  3  5  7  8  9
1 | 1  1  3  4  7
2 | 2  3  3  3  4  9
3 | 0  0  1  6  8
```

Key: 1|3 = 13 books

The stem and leaf diagram on the left shows the number of books that each of the authors has written.

a) How many authors have written fewer than 10 books?

....

b) What is the range of the data?

....

The diagram below is a back-to-back stem and leaf diagram. It shows the number of crime fiction books written by some of the authors, sorted by their age.

c) What was the greatest number of crime fiction books written by an author aged 40+?

....

d) How much greater is the median of the 40+ authors than the median of the Under 40 authors?

....

40+		Under 40		
2	0	3	5	6
9	1	1	1	4	7
7 3	2	2	3	8

Key: 2|8 = 28 books for Under 40
     3|2 = 23 books for 40+

How did you do?

Just so you know — frequency diagrams are a type of 'histogram'. But let's not get too bogged down in the lingo. Once you're all done with these two pages, you should feel like you're able to:

☐ Interpret and construct frequency diagrams and polygons.

☐ Interpret and construct stem and leaf diagrams.

Scatter Graphs

1. Yusuf weighs 50 lemons, then squeezes each of them and measures the volume of juice produced. Most of his results are shown in the scatter graph.

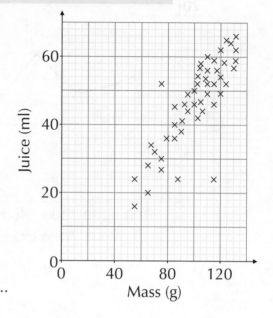

a) The final lemon has a mass of 124 g and produced 56 ml of juice.
Plot the data for this lemon on the graph.

b) Draw a line of best fit for the data and use it to estimate the mass of a lemon that produced 25 ml of juice.

.... g

c) Yusuf says: "The graph shows that a bigger **orange** will also generally give me more juice."

Is he right? Explain why.

....

....

2. The scatter graph below shows some information about 25 hens.

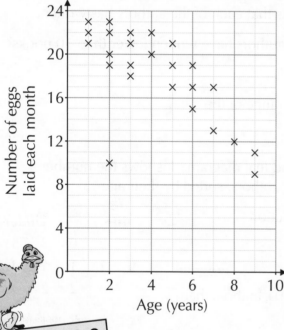

a) Describe the correlation between the ages of the hens and the number of eggs that they lay each month. Explain what this means.

....

....

....

b) One of the data values is an outlier. Circle the outlier on the graph.

c) Work out the range of the ages of the hens.

.... years

How did you do?

You're getting more and more eggs-perienced with handling data on scatter graphs. You're really eggs-ceeding all eggs-pectations. I'm not over-egging it, am I? Anyway, just check that you can:

- [ ] Plot and interpret scatter graphs, including using correlation.
- [ ] Draw lines of best fit and use them to estimate data values.
- [ ] Spot outliers on scatter graphs.

Section Five — Probability and Statistics

Averages and Range from Tables

1. The grouped frequency table below shows information on the areas of 30 parks.

Area (a hectares)	$0 < a \leq 30$	$30 < a \leq 60$	$60 < a \leq 90$	$90 < a \leq 120$	$120 < a \leq 150$	Total
Frequency (f)	4	3	7	10	6	30
Mid-interval value (m)	....	....	....	....	....	—
$f \times m$	....	....	....	....	....	....

a) Write down the modal class.

....

b) Which class contains the median?

....

c) (i) Complete the table.

(ii) Work out an estimate for the mean area.

Estimate the mean by dividing the total from the f × m row by the total from the frequency row.

.... hectares

2. The table shows the number of hours of sleep that workers in an office say they got last night.

Number of hours of sleep	4	5	6	7	8	9	10
Frequency	3	4	6	5	1	1	0

a) What is the range?

.... hours

b) Work out the median number of hours of sleep.

.... hours

c) One of the workers claims that the mean number of hours of sleep is the same as the mode for this data. Are they correct? Show your working below.

Averages and Range from Tables

3. Rita went into a number of restaurants and counted how many dessert options were available. She has summarised the results in the table below.

Number of desserts	Frequency
0-3	4
4-5	2
6-7	7
8-9	1

a) Find the group that contains the median.

....

b) What is the smallest possible range of the data?

....

4. The time it takes 40 monkeys to each peel 10 bananas is recorded in this table.

Time (t seconds)	Frequency
$20 \le t < 40$	9
$40 \le t < 60$	14
$60 \le t < 80$	11
$80 \le t < 100$	6

a) (i) Find the maximum possible range of the times taken.

.... seconds

(ii) If you knew that the longest time taken by a monkey to peel the bananas was 89 seconds, what would the maximum possible range be?

.... seconds

b) (i) Use the values in the table to estimate the mean time taken by the monkeys.

Add a couple of extra columns to the table to help you find the mean.

.... seconds

(ii) Explain why it isn't possible to calculate the actual mean time taken.

....

....

....

How did you do?

Frequency tables can be a really useful way of tidying up your data — but they're no good if you don't know how to work out averages from them. Before you continue, check that you can:

☐ Find the mean, median, mode and range from frequency tables.

☐ Find or estimate averages and the range from grouped frequency tables.

Section Five — Review Exercise

It's almost time to call it quits — you've got this far and the finishing line is in sight. But before you head off, you'd better play it safe and do these final questions just to be sure it's all sunk in.

1. The stem and leaf diagram on the right shows the number of worms that each of the pupils in a class collected one day.

1	4 8 9 9
2	1 2 2 4
3	0 5 6 6 6
4	1 5 9
5	0

Key: 1 | 4 = 14 worms

   a) How many pupils are in the class?

   ....

   1 mark

   b) What is the range of the number of worms caught?

   ....

   1 mark

   c) Work out the difference between the median number of worms caught and the modal number.

   ....

   2 marks

2. All the zebras in a dazzle are weighed and the length of the left foreleg of each is measured. The results are shown in the scatter graph.

A group of zebras can be called a 'dazzle', a 'herd' or a 'zeal'.

   a) Curtis says that the scatter graph shows **strong positive** correlation. Do you agree? Explain why.

   ....

   ....

   ....

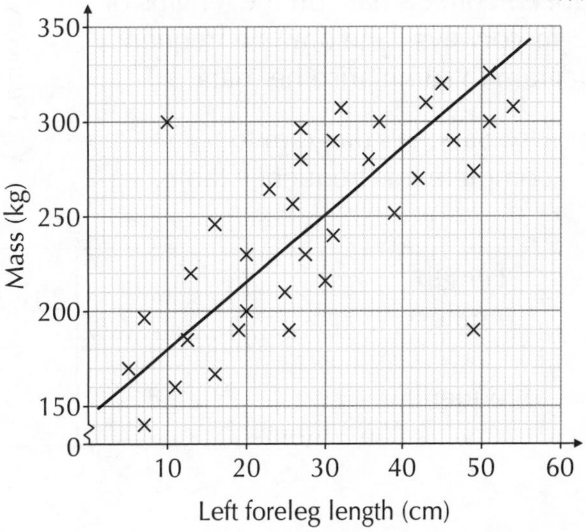

   1 mark

Mass (kg) vs Left foreleg length (cm)

   b) Use the line of best fit drawn on the scatter graph to estimate the mass of a zebra with a left foreleg of length 47 cm.

   .... kg

   1 mark

   c) Write down the left foreleg length and the mass of any outliers.

   ....

   ....

   2 marks

Section Five — Review Exercise

3. A spinner has five sections, labelled 1 to 5.
Gregory spins the spinner 50 times.
The results are shown in the table.

Result	1	2	3	4	5
Frequency	9	18	2	6	15

a) Estimate, as a decimal, the probability that the spinner will land on 4.

.... ☐
1 mark

b) Bea spins a different spinner 80 times. She uses the results to correctly
estimate that the probability of the spinner landing on 4 is 0.2.
How many times did her spinner land on 4?

.... ☐
1 mark

4. A biased 4-sided dice, labelled 1-4, is thrown. The table on
the right shows the probability of it landing on each of its sides.
Some of the entries have been eaten by a zebra.

The probability that it lands on 1 is double the probability that
it lands on 4. Find the probability that the dice lands on 1.

Result	Probability
1	
2	0.2
3	0.5
4	

.... ☐
2 marks

5. Sabeen collects data on the lengths of
42 motorways. She draws a frequency
diagram to summarise her data.

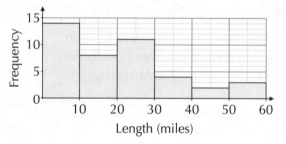

a) Use Sabeen's diagram to
complete this frequency table.

Length (l miles)	....	....	$20 < l \le 30$	$30 < l \le 40$	....	....
Frequency	....	8	11	....	....	....

☐
2 marks

b) Work out an estimate for the mean length of the motorways.
Give your answer to the nearest whole number of miles.

.... miles ☐
3 marks

Answers

Section One — Number

Page 4 — Before you Start

1 a) (i) 1 bag = 0.25 kg = $\frac{1}{4}$ kg, so 4 bags = 1 kg and
4 kg = 4 × 4 = **16 small bags**.

(ii)
```
    4 9 5
  ×   1 6
  2 9⁵7³0
  +4 9 5 0
    7 9 2 0
      ₁ ₁
```
So it cost **£79.20**.

You could also do 16 × £5, then subtract 16 lots of 5p.

b) A large bag is 1 kg, so 4 large bags is 4 kg.
```
   1 7 1 5      7⁸9.¹2 0
 ×       4    − 6 8 . 6 0    So 4 large bags cost £68.60,
 6²8 6²0        1 0 . 6 0    saving £10.60.
```

2 a) 3.056 = **3.06** (to 2 d.p.)

b) 1349 = **1300** (to 2 s.f.)

3 $4^2 - \sqrt{100} + 4 \div 2 = 16 - 10 + 2 = \mathbf{8}$

4 $1000 = \mathbf{10^3}$ $50\,000 = 5 \times 10\,000 = \mathbf{5 \times 10^4}$

5 a) $2^2 \times 3 \times 5 = 4 \times 15 = \mathbf{60}$

b) $3^2 \times 5^2 = 9 \times 25 = \mathbf{225}$

Pages 5-6 — Number Problems

1 a)
```
 ⁵6̸⁵⁵.¹⁴0̸⁹8̸9̸⁹4
  −4 6 . 5 9 5
   1 8 . 4 9 9
```
b)
```
 0 .⁰1̸⁰0̸³3̸.⁶6̸¹⁵5
 − 0 . 0 9 8 6 7
   0 . 0 0 4 9 8
```

2
```
   5 1 8 . 1 6 m
 +  7 4 . 9 8 m
   5 9 3 . 1 4 m
       ₁ ₁ ₁
```

3 **253.4334**
*There is a total of 4 digits following the decimal points in both
the calculation 8.17 × 31.02 and the answer 253.4334.*

4 a)
```
        1 6 6
  1 3 ⌐2 1 5 8
     − 1 3 ↓
       0 8 5 ↓
      − 0 7 8 ↓
        0 7 8
      − 0 7 8
            0
```

b) (i) 2158 ÷ 13 = 166, so £21.58 ÷ 13 = **£1.66**

(ii) 13 = 2 × 5 + 3
```
     7 . 4 9    1 . 6 6    1 4 . 9 8    ¹²2̸¹.⁰¹5̸ 8
   ×     2    ×     3    + 4 . 9 8    − 1 9 . 9 6
    1 4 . 9 8    4 . 9 8    1 9 . 9 6    0 1 . 6 2
        ₁          ₁ ₁        ₁ ₁
```

So Salma could have saved **£1.62**.

*To buy 13 tulips using the deal, Salma would need to buy
2 lots of 5 tulips (2 × £7.49) and 3 individual tulips
(3 × £1.66).*

5
```
   3 6 . 2 8      5 4 . 5 1
   9 0 . 7 2    1 1 5 . 3 9     So Kevin ☑ is moving
 +2 7 5 . 5 0    +2 3 6 . 7 9    the heavier set of items.
   4 0 2 . 5 0    4 0 6 . 6 9
   ₂ ₁ ₁   ₁      ₁ ₁ ₁   ₁
```

6 Brand A:
```
     2 4          1 . 2 5      24 cans weigh 9.6 kg
   ×   4      9 6 ⌐1 2 0 . 0 0   and cost £12 in total.
     9 6        − 9 6 ↓
     ₁            2 4 0 ↓        This is £1.25 per kg.
               − 1 9 2 ↓
                 4 8 0
               − 4 8 0
                     0
```

Brand B:
```
     3 5          1 . 2      6 cans weigh 2.1 kg
   ×   6      2 1 0 ⌐2 5 2 . 0   and cost £2.52 in total.
   2 1 0        − 2 1 0 ↓
     ₃            4 2 0        This is £1.20 per kg.
               − 4 2 0
                     0
```

So **Brand B** is cheaper.
*Alternatively, you could start by finding the cost of one can
of each brand and from this find the cost per kg.*

7 $\dfrac{-10 \div -2}{5} = 1$ $\dfrac{5 - -5}{-3 + 8} = 2$ $\dfrac{-(-11) \times 2}{6 + -4} = 11$

Page 7 — Rounding

1 1.6962 = **1.70** to 2 d.p.   0.007395 = 0.007 to **3** d.p.
0.4247 = 0.425 to **3** d.p.   0.007395 = **0.0074** to 4 d.p.

2 32 549 = **32 500** to 3 s.f.   909 520 = **910 000** to 3 s.f.
32 549 = **32 550** to 4 s.f.   909 520 = **909 500** to 4 s.f.

3

	3 s.f.	4 s.f.	5 s.f.
825 624	**826 000**	**825 600**	**825 620**
13.2973	**13.3**	**13.30**	**13.297**
0.094069	**0.0941**	**0.09407**	**0.094069**

4 29 000 s | 29 500 s | ⟨29 999 s⟩ | ⟨30 049 s⟩ | 30 100 s

Round each time to 3 s.f. — only those circled give 30 000 s.

5 **No** — the **smallest possible** height of the bookcase is
1.995 m, which is **greater than 1.95 m**.

Page 8 — Estimating

1 (2 × £2) + £3 + (5 × £2) + £1 = **£18**

2 a) $\dfrac{\sqrt{36.05}}{5.019} \approx \dfrac{\sqrt{36}}{5.0} = \dfrac{6}{5}$ (or $1\frac{1}{5}$)

b) $\dfrac{\sqrt[3]{63.71}}{(3.04)^2} \approx \dfrac{\sqrt[3]{64}}{(3.0)^2} = \dfrac{4}{9}$

3 a) Rounding to 1 d.p. gives: 0.3 × 0.1 = 0.03.
Rounding to 1 s.f. gives: 0.3 × 0.05 = 0.015.
So Chantel has rounded to ☑ **1 d.p.**

b) Rounding to 1 d.p. gives: 0.1 × 0.4 = 0.04.
Rounding to 1 s.f. gives: 0.07 × 0.4 = 0.028.
So Chantel has rounded to ☑ **1 s.f.**

c) Rounding to 1 d.p. gives: 1.5 × 0.6 = 0.9.
Rounding to 1 s.f. gives: 2 × 0.6 = 1.2.
So Chantel has rounded to ☑ **1 s.f.**

4 $\dfrac{66\,040\,000}{4900} \approx \dfrac{70\,000\,000}{5000} = \mathbf{14\,000}$ **cargo vessels**

Page 9 — Rounding Errors

1 a) $13 - 12.546 = \textbf{0.454}$

b) $12.55 - 12.546 = \textbf{0.004}$

2

Actual number	Rounded number	Rounding error
124.65	**125** to **3** s.f.	**0.35**
0.4318	0.432 to **3** s.f.	**0.0002**
7.5391	**7.5** to **2** s.f.	0.0391

3 a) $\textbf{4555 m} \leq n < \textbf{4565 m}$ $\qquad$ $\textbf{4550 m} \leq p < \textbf{4650 m}$
*Naomi's walk is rounded to the nearest 10 m, so the
actual length is up to 10 ÷ 2 = 5 m bigger or smaller.
Peta's walk is rounded to the nearest 100 m, so the
actual length is up to 100 ÷ 2 = 50 m bigger or smaller.*

b) ☑ Naomi walked further than Peta.
☑ Peta walked further than Naomi.
☑ Naomi and Peta walked exactly the same distance.
All three statements are possible as the intervals in a) overlap.

4 a) $\textbf{115} \leq x < \textbf{125}$
*x is rounded to the nearest 10, so the actual value is
up to 10 ÷ 2 = 5 units bigger or smaller.*

b) $\textbf{1.235} \leq y < \textbf{1.245}$
*y is rounded to the nearest 0.01, so the actual value is
up to 0.01 ÷ 2 = 0.005 units bigger or smaller.*

c) $\textbf{0.01235} \leq z < \textbf{0.01245}$
*z is rounded to the nearest 0.0001, so the actual value is
up to 0.0001 ÷ 2 = 0.00005 units bigger or smaller.*

Page 10 — Power Laws

1 $2^3 \times 2^4 = \boxed{2^{3+4}}$ — *when multiplying, you add the powers.*

2 $5^2 \times 5^3 = 5^{\textbf{5}}$ $\qquad 6^4 \times 6^6 = 6^{\textbf{10}}$ $\qquad 4 \times 2^7 = 2^2 \times 2^7 = 2^{\textbf{9}}$
$3^6 \div 3^2 = 3^{\textbf{4}}$ $\qquad 3^a \div 3^2 = 3^{\textbf{a-2}}$ $\qquad a^5 \div a^3 = a^{\textbf{2}}$
When dividing, you subtract the powers.

3 a) $\dfrac{7^4 \times 7^6}{7^5} = \dfrac{7^{4+6}}{7^5} = \dfrac{7^{10}}{7^5} = 7^{10-5} = \textbf{7}^{\textbf{5}}$

b) $(3^7 \div 3^2)^4 = (3^{7-2})^4 = (3^5)^4 = 3^{5 \times 4} = \textbf{3}^{\textbf{20}}$
When raising one power to another, multiply the powers.

4 $\underline{x^2 \times x^3} = x^{2+3} = x^5$ is the odd one out — the rest equal x^6.

5 $5^1 \div 5^1 = 1$ $\quad$ ☑ — *A number divided by itself is 1.*
$5^1 \div 5^1 = 5^0$ $\quad$ ☑ — *Use the power law $5^1 \div 5^1 = 5^{1-1} = 5^0$.*
$5^0 = 0$ $\quad$ ☒ — *This must be false because...*
$5^0 = 1$ $\quad$ ☑ — *....this is true. The first two statements give
two values for the expression $5^1 \div 5^1$ which
must be equal — they are 1 and 5^0.*

6 a) $10^{-2} = 10^0 \div 10^2 = \dfrac{1}{10^2} = \dfrac{1}{100}$

b) $\boxed{10^{-n} = \dfrac{1}{10^n}}$ *As $10^{-2} = \dfrac{1}{100} = \dfrac{1}{10^2}$.*

Pages 11-12 — Standard Form

1 $1.2 \times 10^3 = 1.2 \times 1000 = \boxed{1200}$

2 $200\,000 = 2 \times 100\,000 = \textbf{2} \times \textbf{10}^{\textbf{5}}$
$54\,000 = 5.4 \times 10\,000 = \textbf{5.4} \times \textbf{10}^{\textbf{4}}$
$127\,000 = 1.27 \times 100\,000 = \textbf{1.27} \times \textbf{10}^{\textbf{5}}$
The power of 10 is the number of places the decimal point moves.

3 $\textbf{1.49} \times \textbf{10}^{\textbf{8}} \textbf{ km}$

4 $2.5 \times 10^{-2} = 2.5 \times \dfrac{1}{100} = 2.5 \div 100 = \textbf{0.025}$
$3.84 \times 10^{-3} = 3.84 \times \dfrac{1}{1000} = 3.84 \div 1000 = \textbf{0.00384}$
*The power of 10 is the number of places the decimal point moves.
The power is negative, so the decimal point moves to the left.*

5 $0.05 = \textbf{5} \times \textbf{10}^{\textbf{-2}}$ $\qquad\qquad 0.807 = \textbf{8.07} \times \textbf{10}^{\textbf{-1}}$
$0.00261 = \textbf{2.61} \times \textbf{10}^{\textbf{-3}}$

6 $0.000139 \text{ m} = \textbf{1.39} \times \textbf{10}^{\textbf{-4}} \textbf{ m}$

7 a)

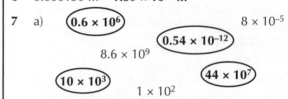

$\boxed{0.6 \times 10^6}$ $\qquad\qquad\qquad\qquad 8 \times 10^{-5}$
$\qquad\qquad\qquad \boxed{0.54 \times 10^{-12}}$
$\qquad\qquad 8.6 \times 10^9$
$\boxed{10 \times 10^3}$ $\qquad\qquad\qquad\qquad\boxed{44 \times 10^7}$
$\qquad\qquad 1 \times 10^2$

*For a number to be in standard form, the number before
the power of 10 must be greater than or equal to 1
but less than 10.*

b) $0.6 \times 10^6 = (6 \div 10) \times 10^6 = \textbf{6} \times \textbf{10}^{\textbf{5}}$
$0.54 \times 10^{-12} = (5.4 \div 10) \times 10^{-12} = \textbf{5.4} \times \textbf{10}^{\textbf{-13}}$
$10 \times 10^3 = (1 \times 10) \times 10^3 = \textbf{1} \times \textbf{10}^{\textbf{4}}$
$44 \times 10^7 = (4.4 \times 10) \times 10^7 = \textbf{4.4} \times \textbf{10}^{\textbf{8}}$

8 $\textbf{2.1} \times \textbf{10}^{\textbf{-6}}, \textbf{1.2} \times \textbf{10}^{\textbf{-5}}, \textbf{1.2} \times \textbf{10}^{\textbf{5}}, \textbf{2.1} \times \textbf{10}^{\textbf{5}}, \textbf{1.2} \times \textbf{10}^{\textbf{6}}$
*First order by the power of ten (e.g. $1.2 \times 10^{-5} < 1.2 \times 10^5$
because $-5 < 5$) and then order by the number in front of
the × sign (e.g. $1.2 \times 10^5 < 2.1 \times 10^5$ because $1.2 < 2.1$).*

9 a)

Colour	Wavelength	Standard Form
Red (R)	0.000000685 m	**6.85 × 10⁻⁷ m**
Green (G)	**0.00000052 m**	5.2 × 10⁻⁷ m
Blue (B)	0.00000046 m	**4.6 × 10⁻⁷ m**

b) $\boxed{\textbf{B G Y R}}$

10 $(3 \times 10^2) \times (2 \times 10^3) = (3 \times 2) \times 10^{2+3} = \textbf{6} \times \textbf{10}^{\textbf{5}}$
$(6 \times 10^6) \div (2 \times 10^3) = \dfrac{6 \times 10^6}{2 \times 10^3} = 3 \times 10^{6-3} = \textbf{3} \times \textbf{10}^{\textbf{3}}$

11 a) $10^{-3} \times 10^{-4} = 10^{-3+-4} = \textbf{10}^{\textbf{-7}}$

b) (i) $(2 \times 10^{-3}) \times (4 \times 10^{-4}) = (2 \times 4) \times (10^{-3} \times 10^{-4})$
$= \textbf{8} \times \textbf{10}^{\textbf{-7}}$

(ii) **0.0000008**
*$0.002 = 2 \times 10^{-3}$ and $0.0004 = 4 \times 10^{-4}$,
so convert the answer to (i) into ordinary form.*

Page 13 — Prime Factors

1 a)

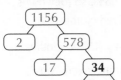

b) **Yes** — because the factor tree shows: $1156 = (2 \times 17)^2$.

2 $\sqrt[3]{29\,791\,000} = 2 \times 5 \times 31 = \boxed{310}$

3 a)

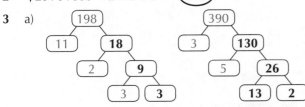

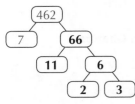

$198 = 2 \times 3^2 \times 11$
$390 = 2 \times 3 \times 5 \times 13$
$462 = 2 \times 3 \times 7 \times 11$
You can write the primes in any order, but it is usual to go from smallest to largest.

b) $2 \times 3 = \mathbf{6}$
2 and 3 are the only common primes in the factorisations of 198, 390 and 462 and they appear once in each number.

4 a) $105 = 3 \times \mathbf{5} \times 7$ and $110 = 2 \times \mathbf{5} \times 11$
The LCM of 105 and 110 is $2 \times 3 \times 5 \times 7 \times 11 = \mathbf{2310}$
The single 5 is a factor of both 105 and 110, so only include it once in the multiplication.

b) $156 = \mathbf{2^2} \times 3 \times 13$ and $234 = 2 \times \mathbf{3^2} \times 13$
The LCM of 156 and 234 is $2^2 \times 3^2 \times 13 = \mathbf{468}$
Remember not to count the common factors more than once.

Pages 14-15 — Review Exercise

1 a) (i)

```
    3 9 1  [1 mark]
19│7 4 2 9
 − 5 7↓
   1 7 2
 − 1 7 1↓
       1 9
     − 1 9
         0
```

(ii) $13 \times 17 \approx \mathbf{10 \times 20 = 200}$ *[1 mark]*
$17 \times 23 \approx \mathbf{20 \times 20 = 400}$ *[1 mark]*
$17 \times 29 \approx \mathbf{20 \times 30 = 600}$ *[1 mark]*
[3 marks available in total — as above]

(iii) $M = \boxed{\mathbf{17 \times 23}}$ *[1 mark]*
$17 \times 23 \approx 400$ is the closest to $M = 391$

b) $7429^3 = (19 \times M)^3 = (17 \times 19 \times 23)^3$
$= \mathbf{17^3 \times 19^3 \times 23^3}$
[2 marks available — 1 mark for using the prime factorisation $7429 = 17 \times 19 \times 23$, 1 mark for the correct answer]

2 $1.045 \leq N < 1.055$
[2 marks available — 2 marks for the correct answer, otherwise 1 mark for 1.045 or 1.055]
N = 1.05 to 3 s.f., so its actual value is up to 0.005 units bigger or smaller.

3 $\dfrac{2^6 \times 2^2}{2^3} = \dfrac{2^{6+2}}{2^3} = \dfrac{2^8}{2^3} = 2^{8-3} = \mathbf{2^5}$ *[1 mark]*

$\dfrac{2^6}{(2^2)^9} = \dfrac{2^6}{2^{2 \times 9}} = \dfrac{2^6}{2^{18}} = 2^{6-18} = \mathbf{2^{-12}}$ *[1 mark]*

[2 marks available in total — as above]

4

	Escape Pod	Cargo Vessel	Battle cruiser
Fuel cap.	142 L	65 100 L	7 080 000 L
Std. form	$\mathbf{1.42 \times 10^2}$ L	$\mathbf{6.51 \times 10^4}$ L	$\mathbf{7.08 \times 10^6}$ L

[3 marks available — 1 mark for each number correctly written in standard form, as shown above]

5 $0.00024, 3.2 \times 10^{-4}, 3.4 \times 10^{-3}, 4.3 \times 10^{-3}, 0.23$ *[1 mark]*

6 a) (i)
```
      6 3 7   [2 marks available — 1 mark for
    ×   5 2   a correct method, 1 mark for the
    1 2 7¹4   correct answer]
  + 3 1¹8³5 0
    3 3 1 2 4
      1 1
```

(ii)
```
       4      52 = 2 × 2 × 13 (or 2² × 13)
  1 3│5⁵2
```
[2 marks available — 2 marks for the correct answer, otherwise 1 mark for any two correct factors]
```
       4 9    637 = 7 × 7 × 13 (or 7² × 13)
  1 3│6⁶3¹¹7
```
[2 marks available — 2 marks for the correct answer, otherwise 1 mark for any two correct factors]
[4 marks available in total — as above]

(iii) $33124 = 2^2 \times 13 \times 7^2 \times 13$
$= 2^2 \times 7^2 \times 13^2 = (2 \times 7 \times 13)^2$
So $52 \times 637 = 33124$ is a square number *[1 mark]*.

b) $\sqrt{52 \times 637} = \sqrt{(2 \times 7 \times 13)^2}$
$= 2 \times 7 \times 13$ *[1 mark]* $= \mathbf{182}$ *[1 mark]*
[2 marks available in total — as above]

7 $70 = 2 \times 5 \times 7$ and $75 = 3 \times 5^2$
The LCM of 70 and 75 is $2 \times 3 \times 5^2 \times 7$, so the comets both pass Earth together again after $2 \times 3 \times 5^2 \times 7 = \mathbf{1050\ years}$.
[3 marks available — 3 marks for the correct answer, otherwise 2 marks for using a correct method to find the LCM or 1 mark for attempting to find a prime factorisation of both numbers]

Section Two — Proportions and Units
Page 16 — Before you Start

1 a) $\frac{3}{5} + \frac{1}{2} = \frac{6}{10} + \frac{5}{10} = \frac{11}{10} = \mathbf{1\frac{1}{10}}$

   b) $\frac{3}{4} \div \frac{5}{9} = \frac{3}{4} \times \frac{9}{5} = \frac{27}{20} = \mathbf{1\frac{7}{20}}$

2 On sale, the bag is 100% – 35% = 65% of its original price, so it costs £24 × 0.65 = **£15.60**.

3 a) 20 : 4 = **5 : 1**
   Divide both sides by 4.

   b) Multiply both sides of the ratio by 10.
   5 : 1 = 50 : 10, so there are **10 woodlice** on the log.

4 Speed = $\frac{\text{distance}}{\text{time}} = \frac{156}{3} = \mathbf{52\ mph}$

5 a) 28 chocolates make 4 gift boxes, so 1 gift box contains 28 ÷ 4 = 7 chocolates. To make 10 gift boxes, Evelyn will need 7 × 10 = **70 chocolates**.

   b) 42 ÷ 7 = **6 gift boxes**

6 12 inches = 1 foot, so 6 inches = 0.5 foot.
   2 feet 6 inches = 2.5 feet
   Then 1 foot ≈ 30 cm, so 2.5 feet ≈ 2.5 × 30 = **75 cm**.

7 20 × 6 = **120 cm**

Pages 17-18 — Fraction Problems

1 a) $\frac{1}{5} + 1\frac{1}{3} = \frac{1}{5} + \frac{4}{3} = \frac{3}{15} + \frac{20}{15} = \frac{\mathbf{23}}{\mathbf{15}}$ or $\mathbf{1\frac{8}{15}}$

   b) $\frac{5}{6} - \frac{3}{4} = \frac{10}{12} - \frac{9}{12} = \frac{\mathbf{1}}{\mathbf{12}}$

   c) $1\frac{3}{7} \times \frac{2}{5} = \frac{10}{7} \times \frac{2}{5} = \frac{20}{35} = \frac{\mathbf{4}}{\mathbf{7}}$

   d) $\frac{2}{9} \div 1\frac{1}{3} = \frac{2}{9} \div \frac{4}{3} = \frac{2}{9} \times \frac{3}{4} = \frac{6}{36} = \frac{\mathbf{1}}{\mathbf{6}}$

2 a) $\frac{1}{3} + \frac{1}{6} = \frac{2}{6} + \frac{1}{6} = \frac{3}{6} = \frac{1}{2}$

   $1 - \frac{1}{2} = \frac{\mathbf{1}}{\mathbf{2}}$ of them vote to go to the park.
   You could have also begun by working out that 6 people wanted to go to the park.

   b) 1 friend is $\frac{1}{12}$ of the group.

   $\frac{3}{4} + \frac{1}{12} = \frac{9}{12} + \frac{1}{12} = \frac{10}{12} = \frac{5}{6}$

   $1 - \frac{5}{6} = \frac{\mathbf{1}}{\mathbf{6}}$ of them vote to go to the park.
   You could have also begun by working out that 2 people now want to go to the park.

3 $\frac{2}{5}$ of a casserole split equally between 4 is
   $\frac{2}{5} \div 4 = \frac{2}{5} \times \frac{1}{4} = \frac{2}{20} = \frac{\mathbf{1}}{\mathbf{10}}$ of the casserole.

4 a) $\frac{3}{8} \times \frac{1}{4} = \frac{\mathbf{3}}{\mathbf{32}}$

   b) $1 - \frac{3}{8} = \frac{5}{8}$ of Paul's collection are not superheroes, so $\frac{5}{8} \times \frac{2}{3} = \frac{10}{24} = \frac{\mathbf{5}}{\mathbf{12}}$ are in mint condition and not superheroes.

5 a) $\frac{4}{9} < \frac{4}{8} = \frac{1}{2} = 50\% < 62.5\%$, so **Joey** owns the greater proportion of red clothes.

   b) $\frac{4}{9}$ of 108 = (108 ÷ 9) × 4 = 48 red clothes.
   $48 \times \frac{1}{6} = \mathbf{8}$ items of clothing given away.

6 $0.8 = \frac{4}{5}$, then $\frac{4}{5} \times 2\frac{3}{4} = \frac{4}{5} \times \frac{11}{4} = \frac{44}{20} = \frac{11}{5} = \mathbf{2\frac{1}{5}\ km}$

7 $\stackrel{\star}{} = 1\frac{5}{12} - \frac{1}{4} = \frac{17}{12} - \frac{3}{12} = \frac{14}{12} = \frac{7}{6}$

   $\bigcirc = 1\frac{1}{8} - \frac{11}{24} = \frac{9}{8} - \frac{11}{24} = \frac{27}{24} - \frac{11}{24} = \frac{16}{24} = \frac{2}{3}$

   $\star \times \bigcirc = \frac{7}{6} \times \frac{2}{3} = \frac{14}{18} = \frac{7}{9}$

   $\star \div \bigcirc = \frac{7}{6} \div \frac{2}{3} = \frac{7}{6} \times \frac{3}{2} = \frac{21}{12} = \frac{7}{4}$

   So the combination is **7, 9, 7, 4**.

Pages 19-20 — Percentage Change

1 10% of 20 = 2, so 5% of 20 = 1.
   So 35% = (3 × 10%) + 5% = 6 + 1 = 7.
   So Tom now has 20 + 7 = **27 badges**.

2 3900 × 1.6 = **6240 m**

3 4 chips is 100% – 90% = 10% of the original amount of chips. So 100% = 4 × 10 = **40 chips**.

4 a) 665 ml is 100% – 30% = 70%.
   So 10% = 665 ÷ 7 = 95 ml.
   So 100% = 95 × 10 = **950 ml**.

   b) 20% of 950 ml = 2 × 10% = 2 × 95 ml = **190 ml**

5 £22 is $\frac{1}{2}$ of £44, so that's 50% off.
   £12 is less than $\frac{1}{2}$ of £30, so that has to be 60% off.
   Finally, £39 is a smaller discount from £60 than from £65, so it's 35% off and 40% off in that order.

6 Increase = £2200 – £1250 = £950
   Percentage increase = $\frac{£950}{£1250} \times 100 = \mathbf{76\%}$

7 a) (i) 2% of £300 = £300 × 0.02 = **£6**

      (ii) 3 × £6 = **£18**

   b) (i) 2% of £500 = £500 × 0.02 = **£10**

      (ii) Interest after 2 years: 2 × £10 = £20
      Money in account = original amount + interest
      = £500 + £20 = **£520**

8 a) $\frac{£75}{£2500} = 0.03 = \mathbf{3\%}$

   b) 1.5% of £1000 = £1000 × 0.015 = £15
   Interest after 2 years = 2 × £15 = £30
   So money in account = £1000 + £30 = **£1030**.

Pages 21-22 — Ratios

1 a) $6:30 = \mathbf{1:5}$
Divide both sides by 6.

b) $18:27 = \mathbf{2:3}$
Divide both sides by 9.

2 There are $3 + 2 = 5$ parts in total so 1 part is $250 \text{ g} \div 5 = 50 \text{ g}$.
$3 \times 50 \text{ g} = \mathbf{150\ g}$ $2 \times 50 \text{ g} = \mathbf{100\ g}$

3 15 lamps are represented by 5 parts, so 1 part is
$15 \div 5 = 3$ items. So there are $2 \times 3 = \mathbf{6\ clocks}$.

4 a) There are 4 times as many long-distance runners, so
for every 1 sprinter, there are 4 long-distance runners.
The ratio of long-distance runners to sprinters is **4:1**.

b) There are $3 + 7 = 10$ parts in total. Of those,
3 parts are long-distance runners, so the fraction of
long-distance runners on Thursdays is $\dfrac{3}{10}$.

5 a) There are $4 + 5 = 9$ parts, so each part represents
$63 \div 9 = 7$ guests. Florence invited 4 parts,
so $4 \times 7 = \mathbf{28\ guests}$.

b) $28 - 8 = 20$ of Florence's guests can make it.
Lewis invited $5 \times 7 = 35$ guests, so $35 - 3 = 32$ of his
guests can make it. The new ratio is $20:32 = \mathbf{5:8}$.

6 a) The ratio is given as a part:whole, so 30 sweets
are represented by 3 parts. So each part is
$30 \div 3 = 10$ sweets. The number of liquorice
sweets is $1 \times 10 = \mathbf{10\ sweets}$.

b) There are $10 - 4 = 6$ liquorice sweets left and
$30 - 4 - 5 = 21$ sweets left in total. So the ratio
is $6:21 = \mathbf{2:7}$.

7 a) Multiplying by 4, $1:1.25 = 4:5$. 12 pizza dishes
are represented by 4 parts, so each part is
$12 \div 4 = 3$ dishes. Pasta dishes are represented by
5 parts, so there are $3 \times 5 = \mathbf{15\ pasta\ dishes}$.
Alternatively, you could have multiplied 12 by 1.25 to get 15.

b) There are $15 + 5 = 20$ dishes that are not pizza.
So the ratio of pizza to non-pizza dishes is
$12:20 = \mathbf{3:5}$.

8 a) $80 \text{ cm}:2 \text{ m} = 80 \text{ cm}:200 \text{ cm} = 2 \text{ cm}:5 \text{ cm} = \mathbf{2:5}$.

b) **1:2.5** — *Divide both sides by 2.*

Page 23 — Direct Proportion

1 4 people need 2 onions and 6 tomatoes, so 1 person
needs $2 \div 4 = \dfrac{1}{2}$ an onion and $6 \div 4 = 1\dfrac{1}{2}$ tomatoes.
So 10 people need $10 \times \dfrac{1}{2} = 5$ onions and
$10 \times 1\dfrac{1}{2} = 15$ tomatoes.

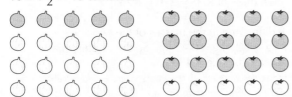

2 4 chameleons can eat 340 bugs in a day,
so 1 chameleon can eat $340 \div 4 = 85$ bugs.
7 chameleons can eat $85 \times 7 = \mathbf{595\ bugs}$.

3 At 0 minutes, no berries have been picked, so the graph
should go through the origin. 540 berries per hour is the
same as 540 berries in 60 minutes. So the worker can pick
$540 \div 6 = 90$ berries in 10 minutes. So the graph should
also go through (10, 90), which the **second graph** does:

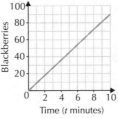

*You could have worked out how many berries were picked in a
different number of minutes. E.g. $540 \div 10 = 54$, so 54 berries
can be picked in 6 minutes and the line should go through (6, 54).*

4 a) 6 mechanics can service 3 cars in a day. Dividing
by 3, 2 mechanics can service $3 \div 3 = 1$ car in a day.
So 2 mechanics can service 5 cars in **5 days**.

b) 6 mechanics can service 3 cars in a day, which means
$m = 6$ when $c = 3$. So $3 = k \times 6 \Rightarrow k = 3 \div 6 = \dfrac{1}{2}$.
So the equation is $c = \dfrac{1}{2}m$.

Page 24 — Inverse Proportion

1 a) It takes 5 cooks 2 hours, so it would take
1 cook 5 times as long: $2 \times 5 = \mathbf{10\ hours}$.

b) 12 cooks would take $10 \div 12 = \dfrac{5}{6}$ of an hour,
which is $\dfrac{5}{6} \times 60 = \mathbf{50\ minutes}$.

2 a) 8 artists take 24 days, so 1 artist
would take $24 \times 8 = \mathbf{192\ days}$.

b) 12 artists take $192 \div 12 = 16$ days to paint the ceiling,
so they would take $16 \times 3 = \mathbf{48\ days}$ to paint the
ceiling 3 times over.

3 a) It would take 1 builder $8 \times 10 = 80$ months.
So it would take 4 builders $80 \div 4 = \mathbf{20\ months}$.

b) 10 builders take 8 months, so $m = 8$ when $b = 10$.
$8 = \dfrac{k}{10} \Rightarrow 8 \times 10 = k \Rightarrow k = 80$
So the equation is $m = \dfrac{80}{b}$.

4 a) 15 fruit-pickers can pick 2400 apples in 20 minutes,
so it would take 1 fruit-picker $15 \times 20 = 300$ minutes.
This means it would take 25 fruit-pickers
$300 \div 25 = \mathbf{12\ minutes}$.

b) 15 fruit-pickers take 20 minutes,
so $t = 20$ when $p = 15$.
$20 = \dfrac{k}{15} \Rightarrow 20 \times 15 = k \Rightarrow k = 300$
So the equation is $t = \dfrac{300}{p}$.

Page 25 — Speed

1 Speed = $\dfrac{\text{distance}}{\text{time}} = \dfrac{90\,\text{m}}{18\,\text{s}} = \textbf{5 m/s}$

Pay attention to the units. You're dividing metres by seconds, so the units should be metres per second (m/s) — not, for instance, miles per hour (mph).

2 a) Distance = speed × time = 0.4 × 45 = **18 m**

b) 5 minutes = 5 × 60 = 300 seconds,
so distance = 0.4 × 300 = **120 m.**

3 a) 2 hours and 15 minutes = 2.25 hours,
so speed = $\dfrac{99}{2.25}$ = **44 mph**.

b) Time = $\dfrac{\text{distance}}{\text{speed}} = \dfrac{70}{44}$ = 1.59... hours
Then 1.59... × 60 = 95.45... minutes
= **95 minutes** (to the nearest minute)

4 a) 1650 metres = 1.65 km, so time = $\dfrac{1.65}{6.6}$ = 0.25 hours.
0.25 × 60 = **15 minutes**

b) **No** — 8:07 pm + 15 minutes = 8:22 pm,
which is later than 8:20 pm.

Page 26 — Density

1 Density = $\dfrac{\text{mass}}{\text{volume}}$, so mass = density × volume.
Mass = 0.24 × 19.6 = 4.704 = **4.7 g** (1 d.p.)

2 Volume = $\dfrac{\text{mass}}{\text{density}} = \dfrac{7500}{7.87}$ = 952.98...
= **950 cm³** (2 s.f.)

3 a) Mass of the water = 1285 – 5 = 1280 kg,
so density = $\dfrac{1280}{1.28}$ = **1000 kg/m³**.

b) Mass = density × volume = 1000 × 0.95 = **950 kg**

4 a) Mass of the steel frame = 8050 × 0.2 = **1610 kg**

b) (i) Volume of the concrete = $\dfrac{4800}{2400}$ = **2 m³**

(ii) Total volume = volume of steel
+ volume of concrete = 0.2 + 2 = **2.2 m³**

Pages 27-28 — Best Buy Problems

1 Fruit 'n' Stuff: 90 ÷ 5 = 18p per banana
Peelies: 16p per banana
So bananas are better value at **Peelies**.

2 a) Small bundle:
3 balloons for £12 —— £3.75 per balloon
£12 ÷ 3 = £4

Medium bundle:
5 balloons for £18 —— £4 per balloon
£18 ÷ 5 = £3.60

Big bundle:
8 balloons for £30 —— £3.60 per balloon
£30 ÷ 8 = £3.75

b) **Medium bundle**

3 a) 300 g packet: 300 ÷ 49 = 6.12... grams per penny
500 g packet: 500 ÷ 75 = 6.66... grams per penny
1 kg packet: 1 kg = 1000 g and £1.60 = 160p,
1000 ÷ 160 = 6.25 grams per penny
You get the most grams per penny in the **500 g packet**.
Alternatively, you could divide the price by the mass to find the price per gram of each packet.

b) £5 = 500p, then 500 ÷ 75 = 6.66...
So Hassan can buy 6 of the 500 g packets,
which is 6 × 500 = **3000 g** of pasta.
Hassan can only buy whole packets of pasta, so you have to round 6.66... down to 6.

4 Foody Favourites: £1.26 ÷ 6 = £0.21 per yoghurt
Dairy Delights: £1.76 ÷ 8 = £0.22 per yoghurt
So **Foody Favourites** are the better value for money.

5 a) For 2 hours, Deal 1 is £15.
2 hours = 2 × 60 = 120 minutes, so for 2 hours
Deal 2 is 12p × 120 = 1440p = £14.40.
So **Deal 2** is the better value for money.

b) For 2 hours 45 minutes, Deal 1 is £15 + (8p × 45)
= £15 + £3.60 = £18.60.
2 hours 45 minutes = 165 minutes, so for 2 hours
45 minutes Deal 2 is 165 × 12 = 1980p = £19.80.
No — Dexter should not choose the same deal.

6 a) Shop A: 9 × £1.20 = £10.80
Shop B: (4 × £2.20) + £1.50 = £10.30
So **Shop B** is the better value for money.

b) 8 pots from Shop B cost 4 × £2.20 = £8.80 and
1 pot from Shop A costs £1.20. £8.80 + £1.20 = £10.

7 a) Kickback Flicks: 12 months – 1 month free
= 11 months, 11 × £6.50 = £71.50.
Amazing TV Time: 12 months – 3 months free
= 9 months, 9 × £7.80 = £70.20.

So **Amazing TV Time** will be the better value
for money.

b) Kickback Flicks: 24 months – 1 month free
= 23 months, 23 × £6.50 = £149.50.
Amazing TV Time: 24 months – 3 months free
= 21 months, 21 × £7.80 = £163.80.

£163.80 – £149.50 = **£14.30**

Page 29 — Metric and Imperial Conversions

1 1.75 hours = 1.75 × 60 = **105 minutes**
= 105 × 60 = **6300 seconds**
4.5 kg = 4.5 × 1000 = 4500 g ≈ 4500 ÷ 450 = **10 pounds**
374 mm = 374 ÷ 10 = **37.4 cm**
= 37.4 ÷ 100 = **0.374 m**
32 pints = 32 ÷ 8 = **4 gallons**

2 Mass of LHS = 3 lb + 1 lb + 2 lb = 6 lb
1 lb ≈ 0.45 kg, so 6 lb = 6 × 0.45 = 2.7 kg.
Known mass of RHS = 270 g + 2 kg
= 0.27 kg + 2 kg = 2.27 kg
The difference in the masses of the two sides is
2.7 kg – 2.27 kg = 0.43 kg. So the mystery mass
is at least 0.43 kg = **430 g**.
If the scales were equal, the mystery box would have a mass of 430 g. Any less than this and the left-hand side would have a greater mass than the right-hand side.

3 a) 500 mm² = 500 ÷ 10² = **5 cm²**

b) 0.204 m³ = 0.204 × 100³ = **204 000 cm³**

4 a) Distance = speed × time = 18 × 1 = **18 km**
18 km = 18 × 1000 = **18 000 m**

b) 1 hour = 3600 seconds, so Yasmina's speed
is 18 000 ÷ 3600 = **5 m/s.**

Answers

Page 30 — Maps and Map Scales

1 3 cm represents 3 × 50 = 150 cm = **1.5 m**.
25 mm represents 25 × 50 = 1250 mm = **1.25 m**.
35 cm is represented by 35 ÷ 50 = 0.7 cm = **7 mm**.

2 a) The road measures 6 cm on the map, so
the scale is 6 cm = 72 km. Dividing both
sides by 6, this is **1 cm = 12 km**.

b) To write the scale as a ratio, the units need
to be the same on both sides.
12 km = 12 × 1000 = 12 000 m
12 000 m = 12 000 × 100 = 1 200 000 cm
So 1 cm = 12 km is 1 cm = 1 200 000 cm,
i.e. **1 : 1 200 000**.

c) 36 km is 36 ÷ 12 = 3 cm on the map.
So Tootins should be 3 cm away from point A
at a 65° angle from the north line:

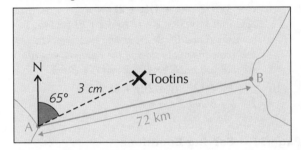

3 a) The scale is 1 cm = 6 miles,
so 24 miles = 24 ÷ 6 = 4 cm.
West is 90° anticlockwise from north:

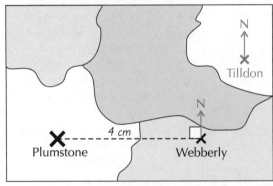

b) (i) Tilldon to Webberly is 2.5 cm on the map,
so it's 6 × 2.5 = **15 miles** in real life.

(ii) The anticlockwise angle from Tilldon to Webberly
is 150°. So the bearing of Webberly from Tilldon
is 360° − 150° = **210°**.

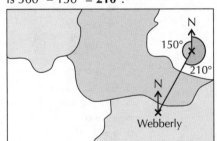

Any angle between 205° and 215° is acceptable.

Pages 31-32 — Review Exercise

1 a) In the ratio 5 : 2, 80 toys are represented by 5 parts.
80 ÷ 5 = 16 *[1 mark]*, so she needs
16 × 2 = **32 sweets** *[1 mark]*.
[2 marks available in total — as above]

b) (i) $\frac{1}{16} \times \frac{1}{3}$ *[1 mark]* $= \frac{1}{16 \times 3} = \frac{1}{48}$ *[1 mark]*
[2 marks available in total — as above]

(ii) $\frac{1}{16} + \frac{1}{48} = \frac{3}{48} + \frac{1}{48} = \frac{4}{48} = \frac{1}{12}$ *[1 mark]*

2 £1740 is 145%, so 1% = 1740 ÷ 145 = £12. *[1 mark]*
So 100% = £12 × 100 = **£1200**. *[1 mark]*
[2 marks available in total — as above]

3 a) 690 words an hour is 690 words in 60 minutes, so he
can write 690 ÷ 60 = 11.5 words per minute. *[1 mark]*
In 14 minutes, he can write
14 × 11.5 = **161 words**. *[1 mark]*
[2 marks available in total — as above]

b) 1725 ÷ 11.5 *[1 mark]* = 150 minutes
= 2 hours 30 minutes *[1 mark]*
[2 marks available in total — as above]

4 a) 4 backpackers can clean 80 cars per day, so
1 backpacker can clean 80 ÷ 4 = 20 cars per day
[1 mark]. The number of backpackers needed to clean
140 cars in a day is 140 ÷ 20 = **7** *[1 mark]*.
[2 marks available in total — as above]

b) 6 backpackers can clean 144 cars per day. If there are
only 2 backpackers, there are $\frac{1}{3}$ as many, so it will
take 3 times as long. 1 day × 3 = **3 days** *[1 mark]*.
*Alternatively you could find how many cars 2 backpackers can
clean in a day (144 ÷ 3 = 48 cars) and divide the number of
cars by this to find the number of days (144 ÷ 48 = 3 days).*

5 a) Speed = $\frac{12}{40}$ = **0.3 m/s** *[1 mark]*

b) Distance = 0.4 × 17 = **6.8 m** *[1 mark]*

6 Density = $\frac{520}{27}$ = 19.259... = **19.3 g/cm³** (1 d.p.)
*[2 marks available — 1 mark for the correct answer,
1 mark for the correct units]*

7 a) Bountiful Biscuits: 400 ÷ 122 = 3.27... grams per penny
Cookie Crumbs: 250 ÷ 90 = 2.77... grams per penny
So the biscuits are better value at **Bountiful Biscuits**.
*[2 marks available — 1 mark for a correct method,
1 mark for the correct conclusion]*
*Alternatively you could divide the price by the mass
to find the price per gram.*

b) (i) 0.045 m² = 0.045 × 100² = **450 cm²** *[1 mark]*

(ii) 0.045 m² = 0.045 × 1000² = **45 000 mm²** *[1 mark]*

8 a) 30 km ÷ 20 km = 1.5, so Yolk should be marked
1.5 cm north of Eggford:

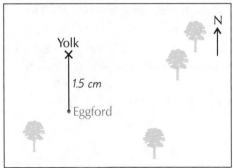

[1 mark]

b) 5 miles ≈ 5 × 1.6 = 8 km *[1 mark]*
8 km ÷ 20 km = 0.4, so they would be
0.4 cm apart on the map *[1 mark]*.
[2 marks available in total — as above]

Section Three — Algebra and Graphs

Page 33 — Before you Start

1 $5(p + 6) = (5 \times p) + (5 \times 6) = \mathbf{5p + 30}$

$2(7 - q) = (2 \times 7) + (2 \times -q) = \mathbf{14 - 2q}$

2 $r - 15rs = \mathbf{r(1 - 15s)}$ $\qquad$ $16t^2 - 8u = \mathbf{8(2t^2 - u)}$

3 a) $3(x + 6) = 4x \Rightarrow 3x + 18 = 4x$

$\qquad\qquad\qquad\qquad \Rightarrow \mathbf{x = 18}$

b) $\dfrac{36 - 4y}{2} = 6 \Rightarrow 36 - 4y = 12$

$\qquad\qquad\qquad \Rightarrow 24 = 4y \Rightarrow \mathbf{y = 6}$

4 a) $\mathbf{l = 20h}$

b) The bucket can hold 5000 ml. Substitute $l = 5000$ into the formula and solve for h. $5000 = 20h \Rightarrow h = 250$. So the bucket is full after **250 hours**.

5 a)

n	1	2	3	4	5
$7n$	7	14	21	28	35
$7n + 10$	17	24	31	38	45

So the expression for the nth term is $\mathbf{7n + 10}$.

b) $(7 \times 20) + 10 = 140 + 10 = \mathbf{150}$

6

x	0	1	2	3
y	**3**	**7**	**11**	**15**

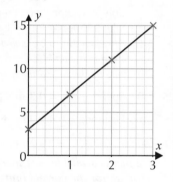

Page 34 — Expanding Brackets

1 $-2(x + 1) = (-2 \times x) + (-2 \times 1) = \mathbf{-2x - 2}$

$x(x + 1) = (x \times x) + (x \times 1) = \mathbf{x^2 + x}$

$-x(2 - 3x) = (-x \times 2) + (-x \times -3x) = \mathbf{-2x + 3x^2}$

2 $(x + 1)(x + 2) = (x \times x) + (x \times 2) + (1 \times x) + (1 \times 2)$

$\qquad\qquad\qquad = \mathbf{x^2 + 2x + x + 2}$

$\qquad\qquad\qquad = \mathbf{x^2 + 3x + 2}$

3 a) $(w + 2)(w + 2) = w^2 + 2w + 2w + 4 = \mathbf{w^2 + 4w + 4}$

b) $(x + 3)(x + 6) = x^2 + 6x + 3x + 18 = \mathbf{x^2 + 9x + 18}$

c) $(y + 1)(2y + 1) = 2y^2 + y + 2y + 1 = \mathbf{2y^2 + 3y + 1}$

d) $(z + 4)(z - 4) = z^2 - 4z + 4z - 16 = \mathbf{z^2 - 16}$

4 a) $\mathbf{(2x + 5)(x - 2)}$

b) $(2x + 5)(x - 2) = 2x^2 - 4x + 5x - 10 = \mathbf{2x^2 + x - 10}$

5 a) $(p + 3)^2 = (p + 3)(p + 3) = p^2 + 3p + 3p + 9$

$\qquad\qquad\qquad\qquad\qquad = \mathbf{p^2 + 6p + 9}$

b) $(q - 1)^2 = (q - 1)(q - 1) = q^2 - q - q + 1$

$\qquad\qquad\qquad\qquad\qquad = \mathbf{q^2 - 2q + 1}$

Page 35 — Factorising

1 $6w + 3wx = \mathbf{3w(2 + x)}$ $\qquad$ $4y - 12yz = \mathbf{4y(1 - 3z)}$

2 $14a + 7ab = \mathbf{7a(2 + b)}$ $\qquad$ $15cd - 20c = \mathbf{5c(3d - 4)}$

$-5e - 35ef = \mathbf{-5e(1 + 7f)}$ or $\mathbf{5e(-1 - 7f)}$

$18g^2 - 2gh = \mathbf{2g(9g - h)}$

3 $27rs + 12rst + 15r^2 = \mathbf{3r(9s + 4st + 5r)}$

4 $6x + 8xy + 10xz = \mathbf{2x(3 + 4y + 5z)}$

$5u + 25uv - 15u^2 = \mathbf{5u(1 + 5v - 3u)}$

5 a) ☑ **3**

The last terms in $x + 1$ and $x + $ ☆ must multiply to give the last term in $x^2 + 4x + 3$. Hence $1 \times$ ☆ $= 3$ and so ☆ $= 3$.

b) ☑ **5**

The last terms in $x + $ ☆ and $x + 1$ must multiply to give the last term in $x^2 + 6x + 5$. Hence ☆ $\times 1 = 5$ and so ☆ $= 5$.

6 a) $x^2 + 3x + 2 = \mathbf{(x + 1)(x + 2)}$

You want $x^2 + 3x + 2 = (x + A)(x + B)$ for two numbers A and B. By expanding these brackets and comparing both sides of the equation, you can see that you need $A \times B = 2$ and $A + B = 3$.

b) $y^2 + 8y + 12 = \mathbf{(y + 2)(y + 6)}$

$2 + 6 = 8$ and $2 \times 6 = 12$

Page 36 — Solving Equations

1 a) $13w + 9 = 6w + 30 \Rightarrow 13w - 6w = 30 - 9$

$\qquad\qquad\qquad\qquad\qquad \Rightarrow 7w = 21$

$\qquad\qquad\qquad\qquad\qquad \Rightarrow \mathbf{w = 3}$

b) $21x + 1 = 4(9 + 4x) \Rightarrow 21x + 1 = 36 + 16x$

$\qquad\qquad\qquad\qquad\qquad \Rightarrow 21x - 16x = 36 - 1$

$\qquad\qquad\qquad\qquad\qquad \Rightarrow 5x = 35$

$\qquad\qquad\qquad\qquad\qquad \Rightarrow \mathbf{x = 7}$

c) $2(3y - 2) = 6 + 7y \Rightarrow 6y - 4 = 6 + 7y$

$\qquad\qquad\qquad\qquad\qquad \Rightarrow 7y - 6y = -4 - 6$

$\qquad\qquad\qquad\qquad\qquad \Rightarrow \mathbf{y = -10}$

d) $3(1 + 3z) = -2(5 - 4z) \Rightarrow 3 + 9z = -10 + 8z$

$\qquad\qquad\qquad\qquad\qquad \Rightarrow 9z - 8z = -10 - 3$

$\qquad\qquad\qquad\qquad\qquad \Rightarrow \mathbf{z = -13}$

2 a) $\dfrac{16}{3} = 2(u + 2) \Rightarrow 16 = 6(u + 2)$

$\qquad\qquad\qquad\qquad \Rightarrow 16 = 6u + 12$

$\qquad\qquad\qquad\qquad \Rightarrow 4 = 6u$

$\qquad\qquad\qquad\qquad \Rightarrow u = \dfrac{4}{6}$, so $\mathbf{u = \dfrac{2}{3}}$

b) $5(1 - \frac{2}{5}v) = 7(2 - v) \Rightarrow 5 - 2v = 14 - 7v$

$\qquad\qquad\qquad\qquad \Rightarrow -2v + 7v = 14 - 5$

$\qquad\qquad\qquad\qquad \Rightarrow 5v = 9$

$\qquad\qquad\qquad\qquad \Rightarrow \mathbf{v = \dfrac{9}{5}}$ or $\mathbf{1\dfrac{4}{5}}$

3 a) $3q - 1 = \dfrac{3q + 4}{2} \Rightarrow 2(3q - 1) = 3q + 4$

$\qquad\qquad\qquad\qquad \Rightarrow 6q - 2 = 3q + 4$

$\qquad\qquad\qquad\qquad \Rightarrow 6q - 3q = 4 + 2$

$\qquad\qquad\qquad\qquad \Rightarrow 3q = 6$

$\qquad\qquad\qquad\qquad \Rightarrow \mathbf{q = 2}$

b) $\dfrac{2(r + 1)}{5} = \dfrac{r + 3}{3} \Rightarrow 6(r + 1) = 5(r + 3)$

$\qquad\qquad\qquad\qquad \Rightarrow 6r + 6 = 5r + 15$

$\qquad\qquad\qquad\qquad \Rightarrow 6r - 5r = 15 - 6$

$\qquad\qquad\qquad\qquad \Rightarrow \mathbf{r = 9}$

c) $t - 2 + \dfrac{t+1}{4} = 12 \Rightarrow 4(t-2) + t + 1 = 4 \times 12$
$\Rightarrow 4t - 8 + t + 1 = 48$
$\Rightarrow 5t - 7 = 48$
$\Rightarrow 5t = 55$
$\Rightarrow \boldsymbol{t = 11}$

Pages 37-38 — Inequalities

1 n is less than 6: $\boldsymbol{n < 6}$
n is greater than or equal to 6: $\boldsymbol{n \geq 6}$

2 $\boxed{20 < S < 30}$

3 $p \leq 4$: **1, 2, 3, 4** $p < 6$: **1, 2, 3, 4, 5**
$2 < p \leq 5$: **3, 4, 5** $1 \leq p \leq 3$: **1, 2, 3**

4 a)

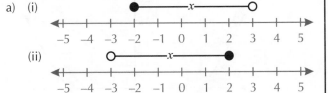

b) $\boldsymbol{3 \leq x \leq 6}$ or $\boldsymbol{3 \leq x < 7}$ or $\boldsymbol{2 < x \leq 6}$ or $\boldsymbol{2 < x < 7}$

5 $-4 < N \leq 3$
When drawing inequalities, an open circle is used for < or >
and a closed circle is used for ≤ or ≥.

6 $\boldsymbol{7 \leq a < 18}$ $\boldsymbol{13 < b < 24}$

7 a) (i)

```
  ●━━━━━x━━━━━○
◄━┼━┼━┼━┼━┼━┼━┼━┼━┼━┼━►
 -5 -4 -3 -2 -1  0  1  2  3  4  5
```

(ii)

```
  ○━━━━━x━━━━━●
◄━┼━┼━┼━┼━┼━┼━┼━┼━┼━┼━►
 -5 -4 -3 -2 -1  0  1  2  3  4  5
```

b) $\boldsymbol{-2 \leq x \leq 2}$

8 a) $\boldsymbol{0 < y < 10}$

b) ☑ $\dfrac{1}{2}$ and ☑ **9.99**

9 $n + 2 < 7 \Rightarrow n < 7 - 2 \Rightarrow n < 5$
So $n =$ **1, 2, 3** or **4**.

10 a) $w + 1 \leq 5 \Rightarrow w \leq 5 - 1 \Rightarrow \boldsymbol{w \leq 4}$

b) $6 - x > 5 \Rightarrow 6 - 5 > x \Rightarrow \boldsymbol{1 > x}$ (or $\boldsymbol{x < 1}$)

c) $-5 < y - 1 \Rightarrow -5 + 1 < y \Rightarrow \boldsymbol{-4 < y}$ (or $\boldsymbol{y > -4}$)

d) $2z - 1 \geq 1 \Rightarrow 2z \geq 2 \Rightarrow z \geq 2 \div 2 \Rightarrow \boldsymbol{z \geq 1}$

Pages 39-40 — Formulas

1 a) $s = ut = 4 \times (-6) = \boldsymbol{-24}$

b) $s = \dfrac{u - 2t}{4} = \dfrac{4 - 2(-6)}{4} = \dfrac{4 + 12}{4} = \dfrac{16}{4} = \boldsymbol{4}$

2 $\boxed{M = \dfrac{3N}{2} + 1}$

3 a) $\boldsymbol{A = l(w - x)}$ or $\boldsymbol{A = lw - lx}$ b) $\boldsymbol{A = x^2 - \pi r^2}$

4 a) (i) $\boldsymbol{C = 1.8d}$

(ii) $C = 1.8 \times 25 = 45$, so the cost is **£45**.

b) $\boldsymbol{C = 10 + 0.4d}$

---

5 a) $\boldsymbol{y = x - 5}$ b) $\boldsymbol{y = \dfrac{x}{2}}$ c) $\boldsymbol{y = 5x}$

d) $x = 3y - 1 \Rightarrow 3y = x + 1 \Rightarrow \boldsymbol{y = \dfrac{x+1}{3}}$

6 a) $u = 5 - 2v \Rightarrow 2v = 5 - u \Rightarrow \boldsymbol{v = \dfrac{5-u}{2}}$

b) $\boldsymbol{v = \dfrac{u}{2w}}$

c) $w = \dfrac{v-1}{u} \Rightarrow v - 1 = uw \Rightarrow \boldsymbol{v = uw + 1}$

d) $v + u = w - v \Rightarrow 2v = w - u \Rightarrow \boldsymbol{v = \dfrac{w-u}{2}}$

7 a) $p = \sqrt{2q} \Rightarrow 2q = p^2 \Rightarrow \boldsymbol{q = \dfrac{1}{2}p^2}$

b) $p = 1 + q^3 \Rightarrow q^3 = p - 1$
$\Rightarrow \boldsymbol{q = \sqrt[3]{p - 1}}$

8 a) $S = 4\pi r^2 \Rightarrow r^2 = \dfrac{S}{4\pi} \Rightarrow \boldsymbol{r = \sqrt{\dfrac{S}{4\pi}}}$ (or $\boldsymbol{r = \dfrac{1}{2}\sqrt{\dfrac{S}{\pi}}}$)
The radius r is a positive number, so
you only want the positive square root.

b) $r = \sqrt{\dfrac{36\pi}{4\pi}} = \sqrt{9} = \boldsymbol{3 \text{ cm}}$

9 a) $\boldsymbol{P = 35 + 4.5n}$

b) (i) $\boldsymbol{n = \dfrac{P - 35}{4.5}}$

(ii) $n = \dfrac{62 - 35}{4.5} = 6$, so **6 colours** were used.

Page 41 — Sequences

1 1, 3, 9, 27, 81, ... is a **geometric** sequence.
The term-to-term rule is 'multiply by 3'.

5, 8, 11, 14, 17, ... is an **arithmetic** sequence.
The term-to-term rule is 'add 3'.

2, 5, 10, 17, 26, ... is **neither**.
Each term is 1 greater than a square number.

2 **96, 192** and **384**
The term-to-term rule is 'multiply by 2'.

3 a) $6 \div 2 = 3$, so the term-to-term rule is 'multiply by 3'.
Then $N = 6 \times 3 = \boldsymbol{18}$.

b) $162 \times 3 = \boldsymbol{486}$ and $486 \times 3 = \boldsymbol{1458}$ are the next two
terms in the sequence.

4 $64 \div 128 = \dfrac{1}{2}$, so the rule is 'multiply by $\dfrac{1}{2}$' or 'divide
by 2'. So the sequence continues as 4, 2, 1, $\dfrac{1}{2}$, $\dfrac{1}{4}$, ...
The numbers get smaller and smaller but never reach 0.

☐ ... even numbers.   ☑ **... positive numbers.**
☐ ... whole numbers.   ☑ **... non-negative numbers.**

5 a) $\dfrac{11}{2}$, $\dfrac{13}{2}$, $\dfrac{15}{2}$ — *the numerators are the odd numbers.*

b) $\dfrac{6}{7}$, $\dfrac{7}{8}$, $\dfrac{8}{9}$ — *the numerators and denominators*
are going up by 1 each time.

6 After the first two terms, each new term is the
sum of the two terms immediately before it in the
sequence. So to get from 21 to the next term, add
together the terms 13 and 21: $13 + 21 = \boldsymbol{34}$.

Pages 42-43 — Finding the Equation of a Straight Line

A line with equation $y = mx + c$ has gradient = m and y-intercept = c.

1 a) gradient = **2**, y-intercept = **1**

   b) gradient = **–4**, y-intercept = **6**

2 a) $y = 6x - 5$ b) $y = -7x + 8$

3 a) $\frac{4-1}{6-5} = \frac{3}{1} = 3$ b) $\frac{6-8}{0-(-2)} = \frac{-2}{2} = -1$

4 a) E.g. (2, 0) and (4, 1) are two points on the line,
      so the gradient is $\frac{1-0}{4-2} = \frac{1}{2}$.
      You could have used some other points on the line but you should still get the same answer.

   b) ☑ $y = \frac{1}{2}x + 1$ ☑ $y = \frac{1}{2}x$

5

Equation	$y = mx + c$	Grad.	Coordinates of y-intercept
$-5 = y - 6x$	$y = 6x - 5$	6	(0, –5)
$2y - 4x = 6$	$y = 2x + 3$	2	(0, 3)
$\frac{y}{2} + 2x = 3$	$y = -4x + 6$	–4	(0, 6)

The x-coordinate of the y-intercept is always O.

6 The gradient of the line is $\frac{13-3}{2-0} = \frac{10}{2} = 5$ and the
   y-intercept is 3, so the line has the equation $y = 5x + 3$.

7 a) E.g. R passes through (0, 1) and (1, 2), so the
      gradient is $\frac{2-1}{1-0} = \frac{1}{1} = 1$ and the y-intercept is 1.
      So R has the equation $y = x + 1$.

   b) E.g. S passes through (4, 2) and (5, 0), so the
      gradient is $\frac{0-2}{5-4} = \frac{-2}{1} = -2$. So the line has
      the equation $y = -2x + c$ for some number c.
      When $x = 4$, $y = 2$, so $2 = -2 \times 4 + c \Rightarrow c = 10$.
      So S has the equation $y = -2x + 10$.

8 a) E.g. L passes through (–2, 1) and (–1, 3),
      so the gradient is $\frac{3-1}{-1-(-2)} = \frac{2}{1} = 2$.

   b) (i) The gradient of the line will be the same
          as the gradient from part a) since the lines
          are parallel. So the equation is of the form
          $y = 2x + c$ for some number c. The point
          P has coordinates (2, 1), so $1 = 2 \times 2 + c$
          $\Rightarrow c = -3$. So the equation is $y = 2x - 3$.

   (ii)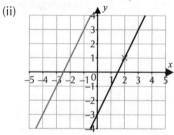

Pages 44-45 — Quadratic Graphs

1 a)

x	–4	–2	0	2	4
x^2	16	4	0	4	16
$y = x^2 + 1$	17	5	1	5	17

   b)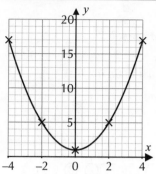

2 a) (i)

x	–5	–3	0	3	5
x^2	25	9	0	9	25
$x^2 - 9$	16	0	–9	0	16

   (ii)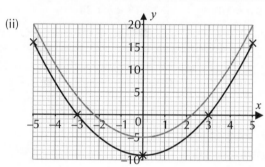

   b) (i) **(0, –5)**

   (ii) The term '– 9' determines the **y-intercept** at $y = -9$.

   (iii) The number at the end of the expression is '+ 2',
        so the coordinates are **(0, 2)**.
        Alternatively, you could substitute in x = O:
        $y = O^2 + O + 2 = 2$

   c) **No** — at any value of x, the y-values
      always differ by $9 - 5 = 4$.

3 The graph looks like an n-shaped quadratic, so the
   equation has a minus sign in front of the x^2. Also, the
   graph has a positive y-intercept, so the equation has a
   '+ C' term for some positive number C.
   The equation must be: $y = -x^2 + 3$ ☑

4 a)

x	0	1	2	3	4	5
y	9	4	1	0	1	4

   b)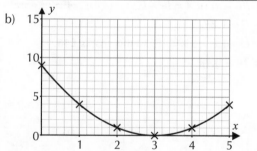

5 $y = x^2$ $\boxed{D}$ — u-shaped and goes through the origin.

$y = -x^2$ $\boxed{B}$ — n-shaped and goes through the origin.

$y = x^2 - 2$ $\boxed{A}$ — u-shaped with a negative y-intercept.

$y = x^2 + 2x + 1$ $\boxed{C}$ — u-shaped and shifted to the left.

6 a)

x	0	1	1.5	2	3
y	−2	0	0.25	0	−2

b)

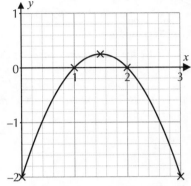

Pages 46-47 — Solving Equations Using Graphs

1 a) Read up from the x-axis, then across to the y-axis.

  (i) **$y = 30$**   (ii) **$y = 80$**

b) Read across from the y-axis, then down to the x-axis.

  (i) **$x = 0$**   (ii) **$x = 2$**

  (iii) **$x = 0.8$**   (iv) **$x = 2.4$**

2 a) **$x = 1$ and $y = 7$**   **b)** **$x = -2$ and $y = 4$**

c) **$x = -0.5$ and $y = 2.5$**

Find the point where the two lines meet
and read off the x- and y-coordinates.

3 a) **$x = -1$ or $x = 3$**

Find the points where the graph of $y = 4x^2 - 8x - 12$
meets the x-axis.

b) (i)

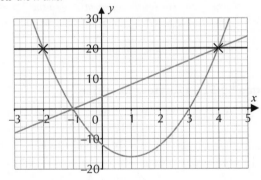

  (ii) **$x = -2$ or $x = 4$**

  Find the points where the graph of $y = 4x^2 - 8x - 12$
  meets the line $y = 20$.

c) The graphs of $y = 4x^2 - 8x - 12$ and $y = 4x + 4$ meet at the points $(-1, 0)$ and $(4, 20)$. So the two solutions are: **$x = -1, y = 0$ and $x = 4, y = 20$**.

4

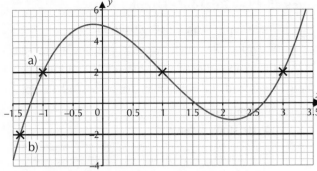

a) **$x = -1, x = 1, x = 3$**

b) The graph of $y = x^3 - 3x^2 - x + 5$ crosses the line $y = -2$ near the point $(-1.4, -2)$, as shown above. So **$x = -1.4$** is an approximate solution to $x^3 - 3x^2 - x + 5 = -2$.

Any value of x between −1.4 and −1.3 is acceptable.

5

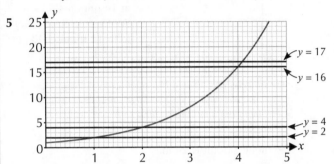

a) (i) **$x = 1$**   (ii) **$x = 4$**

b) (i) The graph of $y = 2^x$ crosses the line $y = 4$ at the point $(2, 4)$, so **$x = 2$** is the solution to $2^x = 4$.

  (ii) The graph of $y = 2^x$ crosses the line $y = 17$ near the point $(4.1, 17)$, so **$x = 4.1$** is an approximate solution to $2^x = 17$.

  Values of x between 4.0 to 4.2 are acceptable.

6 a) **$y = 1$**

b) $y = \dfrac{A}{x} \Rightarrow A = xy$

From part a), when $x = 2$, $y = 1$, so $A = 2 \times 1 = \mathbf{2}$.

c)

The line $y = x$ intersects the graph of $y = \dfrac{2}{x}$ near the point $(1.4, 1.4)$, so **$x = 1.4, y = 1.4$** is an approximate solution to the simultaneous equations.

Values of x and y between 1.3 and 1.5 are acceptable.

Pages 48-49 — Real-Life Graphs

1 | C | The volume of an inflating balloon.

   | D | The price of a watch before, during and after a sale.

   | A | The temperature of a cup of tea if left undrunk.

   | B | The speed of a car travelling at a constant 30 mph.

2 a) (i) **7 minutes**

   (ii) **He slowed down.** ☑
   *The gradient of the graph changes at 7 minutes.
   It gets less steep, so John gets slower at this time.*

   b)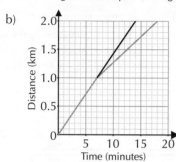
   Extend the graph with a straight line at 7 minutes.
   The extended line reaches 2.0 km at 14 minutes.
   So it would have taken John **14 minutes** to get to work.

   *Answers between 13.5 and 14.5 minutes from the graph
   are acceptable. You could also have calculated the time
   by doubling the time it takes John to travel 1 km:
   7 minutes × 2 = 14 minutes.*

3 a) The highest point is **24 m.**

   b) (i)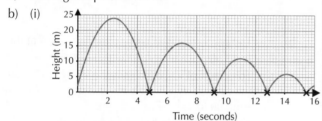

   (ii) The first time is at 4.8 seconds and
   the second time is at 9.2 seconds.
   So there is 9.2 − 4.8 = **4.4 s** between them.

4 a)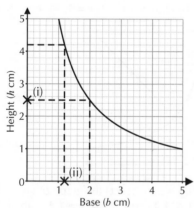

   (i) At $b = 2$ cm, the height is approximately **2.5 cm.**
   Answers between 2.4 cm and 2.6 cm are acceptable.

   (ii) At $h = 4.2$ cm, the base is approximately **1.2 cm.**
   Answers between 1.1 cm and 1.3 cm are acceptable.

   b) The graph passes through (5, 1),
   so $A = \frac{1}{2}bh = \frac{1}{2} \times 5 \times 1 = $ **2.5 cm²**.

5 a) The graph for jar 1 is higher than the graph for jar 2 at
   200 g, so the wax is deeper in **jar 1**.

   b) E.g.
   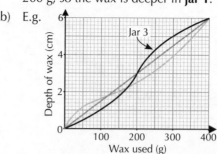

   *Your graph should have the same general shape as the one
   above. The gradient should start off shallow, then become
   steeper, and then become shallow again. Your graph should
   also cross the graph for jar 1 around halfway (200 g) as
   jar 3 is roughly symmetrical.*

6 a)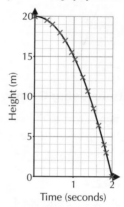

   b) (i) **15 m**
   Answers between 14.5 m and 15.5 m are acceptable.

   (ii) **7 m**
   Answers between 6.5 m and 8.5 m are acceptable.

   c) $h = 20 - 5t^2$

   *The graph crosses the y-axis at 20, so the 20 in the
   equation should be +20, not −20. The graph is n-shaped
   (or it would be if you could see all of it), so the sign in front
   of the t^2 has to be negative.*

Pages 50-51 — Review Exercise

1 a) $(x + 5)(x + 3) = (x \times x) + (x \times 3) + (5 \times x) + (5 \times 3)$
   $= x^2 + 3x + 5x + 15$
   $= x^2 + 8x + 15$ **[1 mark]**

   b) $(p + 7)(2 - p) = (p \times 2) + (p \times -p) + (7 \times 2) + (7 \times -p)$
   $= 2p - p^2 + 14 - 7p$
   $= -p^2 - 5p + 14$ **[1 mark]**

2 $12ab - 6b + 15bc = 3b(4a - 2 + 5c)$ **[1 mark]**

3 a) $6n - 8$ **[1 mark]**

   b) $6n - 8 = \dfrac{7n - 1}{2} \Rightarrow 12n - 16 = 7n - 1$ **[1 mark]**
   $\Rightarrow 12n - 7n = -1 + 16$
   $\Rightarrow 5n = 15$
   $\Rightarrow n = 3$

   So there are **3 balloons** in each packet. **[1 mark]**
   [2 marks available in total — as above]

Answers

4 a) $x - 3 < -1 \Rightarrow x < 2$

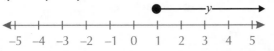

[1 mark]

b) $2y - 1 \geq y \Rightarrow y \geq 1$

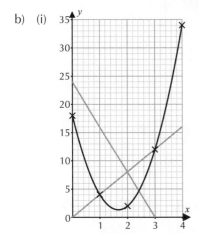

[1 mark]

5 a) $12 - 4 = 8$, so the next two terms are:
$12 + 8 = $ **20** and $20 + 8 = $ **28**.
[2 marks available — 1 mark for each correct term]

b) $12 \div 4 = 3$, so the next two terms are:
$12 \times 3 = $ **36** and $36 \times 3 = $ **108**.
[2 marks available — 1 mark for each correct term]

6 a) $M = 63 - 3.5d$ *[1 mark]*

b) (i) $M = 63 - 3.5d$
$\Rightarrow M + 3.5d = 63 \Rightarrow 3.5d = 63 - M$ *[1 mark]*
$\Rightarrow d = \dfrac{63 - M}{3.5}$ *[1 mark]*

[2 marks available in total— as above]

(ii) Substitute $M = 0$ into the formula: $d = \dfrac{63 - 0}{3.5} = 18$
So Erin runs out of money after **18 days**.
[2 marks available — 1 mark for attempting to substitute $M = 0$, 1 mark for the correct answer]

7 a) $(0, 24)$ and $(3, 0)$ are two points on the line L,
so the y-intercept is $c = 24$ and the gradient is
$m = \dfrac{0 - 24}{3 - 0} = -8$. So the equation is $y = -8x + 24$.
[3 marks available — 1 mark for the correct value of m, 1 mark for the correct value of c, 1 mark for the correct equation in the right form]

b) (i)

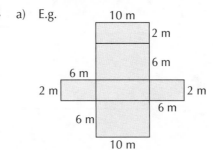

[2 marks available — 1 mark for correctly plotting the points, 1 mark for joining them with a smooth curve]

(ii) The graphs of $y = 4x$ and $y = 6x^2 - 20x + 18$
cross at $x = 1$ *[1 mark]* and $x = 3$ *[1 mark]*.
[2 marks available in total— as above]

8 a) **2 hours** *[1 mark]*

b) The battery charge increases when the phone is plugged in. The battery charge goes from 38% (at 3.6 hours) to 60% (at 5.4 hours).
So the increase is $60 - 38 = $ **22%**.
[2 marks available — 1 mark for a correct method, 1 mark for the correct answer]

Section Four — Geometry
Page 52 — Before you Start

1

2 a) $a = $ **62°** (alternate angles)

b) $b = $ **123°** (vertically opposite angles)

c) $x = $ **65°** (alternate angles)
$y = 180° - 65° - 80° = $ **35°** (angles in a triangle)

3 a) $C = \pi d = \pi \times 80 = 251.327... = $ **251 cm** (3 s.f.)

b) $r = \dfrac{d}{2} = \dfrac{80}{2} = 40$ cm,
$A = \pi r^2 = \pi \times 40^2 = 5026.548... = $ **5030 cm²** (3 s.f.)

4 a) E.g.

b) $V = 10 \times 2 \times 6 = $ **120 m³**

Pages 53-54 — Polygons

1

Shape	Regular	Irregular
Pentagon		A
Hexagon	C	D
Heptagon	B	E

2 $r = 360° - 90° - 90° - 107° = $ **73°**
Remember that the angles in a quadrilateral add up to 360°.

3 a) The interior angles in one triangle add up to **180°**, so the interior angles in a pentagon add up to $3 \times $ **180°** $ = $ **540°**.

b) (i) E.g.

An octagon can be split up into **6** triangles.

(ii) $6 \times 180° = $ **1080°**

4 The shape is a regular hexagon with exterior angle p and interior angle q:
$p = \dfrac{360°}{n} = \dfrac{360°}{6} = $ **60°**
$q = 180° - p = 180° - 60° = $ **120°**

5 Exterior angle $ = \dfrac{360°}{10} = $ **36°**
Interior angle $ = 180° - $ exterior angle $ = 180° - 36° = $ **144°**

6 The polygon has 7 sides, so the sum of the interior angles is $(7 - 2) \times 180° = 900°$.
$x = 900° - 150° - 140° - 120° - 115° - 130° - 100° = $ **145°**
$y = 180° - 145° = $ **35°**

Pages 55-56 — Loci and Constructions

1

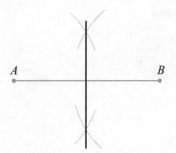

2

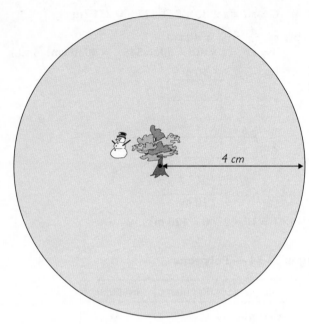

4 cm

3

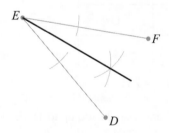

4

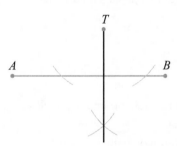

The path should be perpendicular to AB.

Pages 57-59 — Transformations

1

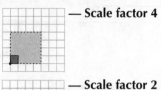

— Scale factor 4

— Scale factor 2

— Scale factor 3

2   a) M to $N = \begin{pmatrix} -4 \\ 6 \end{pmatrix}$ b) N to $M = \begin{pmatrix} 4 \\ -6 \end{pmatrix}$

The values are the same but the direction is reversed by the signs.

3   a) $y = x$

   b)   **180° around point (4, 3)**
        The rotation can be either clockwise or anti-clockwise since it's a half-turn.

   c)   **Scale factor 3, centre (0, 0)** (or **the origin**)

4   The rectangle with the dotted line shows the interim position of the box of cherries after the first translation.

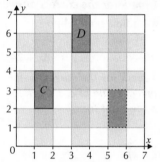

5

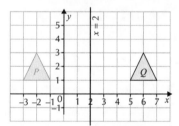

6   a)

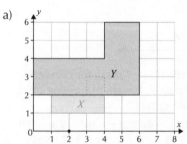

   b)

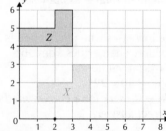

7

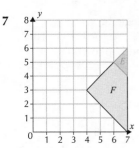

8 a)

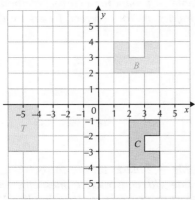

b) **Yes** — she does collide with T,
as shown in the diagram below.

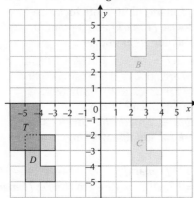

Pages 60-61 — 3D Shapes

1 a) Area of triangular face = $\frac{1}{2}(6 \times 5) = 15$ cm^2
Volume = $15 \times 9 = $ **135 cm^3**

b) Volume = $15 \times 20 = $ **300 mm^3**

c) Volume = $9\pi \times 12 = $ **108π m^3**

d) Area of circular face = $\pi r^2 = \pi \times 1^2 = \pi$ cm^2
Volume = $\pi \times 5 = $ **5π cm^3**

2 Area of circular face = $\pi r^2 = \pi \times 6^2 = 113.097...$ cm^2
Volume = $113.097... \times 20 = 2261.946...$
     = **2261.9 cm^3** (1 d.p.)

3 Volume = cross-sectional area $\times h$, so
$h = \dfrac{\text{volume}}{\text{cross-sectional area}} = \dfrac{72\pi}{6\pi} = $ **12 m**

4 E.g.

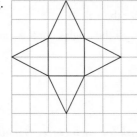

5 Volume of cylinder = area of circular face $\times$ height
     = $\pi \times 1.5^2 \times 15 = 106.028...$ m^3
Volume of cuboid = $3 \times 19 \times 8 = 456$ m^3
Total volume = $106.028... + 456 = 562.028...$
     = **562.0 m^3** (1 d.p.)

6 Circumference of circular face = $2\pi r = 2 \times \pi \times 5$
     = $31.415...$ cm

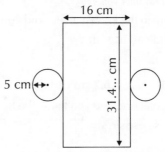

Area of net = area of rectangular face +
     $2 \times$ area of circular face
= $(16 \times 31.415...) + 2(\pi \times 5^2)$
= $502.654... + 157.079... = 659.734...$
= **659.7 cm^2 (1 d.p.)**

Page 62 — Pythagoras' Theorem

1

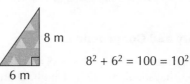

$8^2 + 6^2 = 100 = 10^2$

2 a) $a^2 = b^2 + c^2$
$l^2 = 5^2 + 12^2 = 25 + 144 = 169$
$l = \sqrt{169} = $ **13 cm**

b) $a^2 = b^2 + c^2$
$5^2 = l^2 + 3^2$,
so $l^2 = 5^2 - 3^2 = 25 - 9 = 16$
$l = \sqrt{16} = $ **4 cm**

3 Let the unknown length be x:

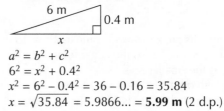

$a^2 = b^2 + c^2$
$6^2 = x^2 + 0.4^2$
$x^2 = 6^2 - 0.4^2 = 36 - 0.16 = 35.84$
$x = \sqrt{35.84} = 5.9866... = $ **5.99 m** (2 d.p.)

Page 63 — Trigonometry

1 a) The two known sides are the opposite
and the hypotenuse, so use $\sin x = \dfrac{O}{H}$.
$\sin t = \dfrac{6}{8}$
$t = \sin^{-1}\left(\dfrac{6}{8}\right) = 48.590... = $ **48.6°** (1 d.p.)

b) The two known sides are the adjacent
and the hypotenuse, so use $\cos x = \dfrac{A}{H}$.
$\cos u = \dfrac{10}{13}$
$u = \cos^{-1}\left(\dfrac{10}{13}\right) = 39.715... = $ **39.7°** (1 d.p.)

c) The two known sides are the opposite
and the adjacent, so use tan $x = \dfrac{O}{A}$.

$\tan v = \dfrac{7}{3}$

$v = \tan^{-1}\left(\dfrac{7}{3}\right) = 66.801... = \textbf{66.8°}$ (1 d.p.)

Use SOH-CAH-TOA to decide which ratio
to use depending on which sides you know.

2 a) Length *DE* is opposite to the known angle, and you
know the adjacent side, so use tan $x = \dfrac{O}{A}$.

$\tan 40° = \dfrac{DE}{8}$

$DE = 8 \times \tan 40° = 6.712... = \textbf{6.7 cm}$ (1 d.p.)

b) Length *DE* is the hypotenuse, and you know the length
of the opposite side, so use sin $x = \dfrac{O}{H}$.

$\sin 50° = \dfrac{9}{DE}$

$DE = \dfrac{9}{\sin 50°} = 11.748... = \textbf{11.7 cm}$ (1 d.p.)

3

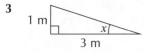

You know the opposite and the adjacent, so use tan $x = \dfrac{O}{A}$.

$\tan x = \dfrac{1}{3}$, $x = \tan^{-1}\left(\dfrac{1}{3}\right) = 18.434... = \textbf{18.4°}$ (1 d.p.)

Page 64 — Similarity and Congruence

1 The criteria for congruence are SSS, AAS, SAS and RHS,
so the only triangles that should be circled are **B**, **D** and **E**.
There's not enough information on the others to decide.

2 The two adjacent sides are known, so compare
these to find the ratio.

$\dfrac{12}{3} = 4$, so triangle Q is 4 times the size of triangle P:

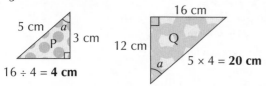

3 The two base lengths are known, so compare these to find
the scale factor. $18 = 6 \times 3$, so the larger trapezium is
3 times as big as the smaller one.
The missing length on the left is $3 \times 3 = \textbf{9 cm}$.
The missing length on the right is $12.3 \div 3 = \textbf{4.1 cm}$.
Similar shapes have the same angles, so the
missing angle is $360° - 82° - 64° - 116° = \textbf{98°}$.

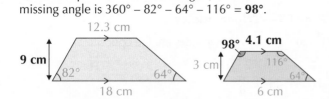

Page 65 — Geometric Relationships

1 a) **180°** (angles on a straight line)

b) E.g. Using alternate angles, the angle *XYZ* is equal to
a, and the angle *XZY* is equal to *c*. *a*, *b* and *c* add up
to 180° from part a), so the angles in the triangle must
also add up to 180°.

2 Let the unknown angle in the triangle be *x*.
Angles in a triangle add up to 180°, so $b + c + x = 180°$.
Angles along a straight line also add up to 180°,
so $a + x = 180°$. This means $a + x = b + c + x$, so $a = b + c$.

Pages 66-67 — Review Exercise

1 $s = \dfrac{360°}{5} = \textbf{72°}$ $t = 180° - 72° = \textbf{108°}$

[3 marks available — 1 mark for a correct method to find
one of the angles, 1 mark for s correct, 1 mark for t correct]

2

[2 marks available — 2 marks for the correct
perpendicular line with construction lines, otherwise
1 mark for at least two correct construction lines]

3 a) **A reflection** *[1 mark]* in the line $y = -1$ *[1 mark]*
[2 marks available — as above]

b) **A rotation** *[1 mark]* of **90° anticlockwise**
/ 270° clockwise *[1 mark]* about point **(0, –2)** *[1 mark]*
[3 marks available — as above]

4 Area of circular face $= \pi r^2 = \pi \times 2.5^2 = 19.634...$ cm²
Volume of can = area of circular face × height
$= 19.634... \times 20 = 392.699...$
$= \textbf{392.7 cm}^3$ (1 d.p.)

[2 marks available — 2 marks for correct answer,
otherwise 1 mark for suitable working]

5 a) $a^2 = b^2 + c^2$
$h^2 = 10^2 + 12^2$ *[1 mark]* $= 100 + 144 = 244$
$h = \sqrt{244} = 15.620... = \textbf{15.6 cm}$ (1 d.p.) *[1 mark]*

b) $a^2 = b^2 + c^2$
$13^2 = j^2 + 7^2$,
so $j^2 = 13^2 - 7^2$ *[1 mark]* $= 169 - 49 = 120$
$j = \sqrt{120} = 10.954... = \textbf{11.0 cm}$ (1 d.p.) *[1 mark]*

[4 marks available in total — as above]

6 a) The two known sides are the adjacent
and the hypotenuse, so use cos $x = \dfrac{A}{H}$

$\cos x = \dfrac{7}{9}$ *[1 mark]*

$x = \cos^{-1}\left(\dfrac{7}{9}\right) = 38.942... = \textbf{38.9°}$ (1 d.p.) *[1 mark]*

b) Length *BC* is opposite to the known angle, and you
know the adjacent side, so use tan $x = \dfrac{O}{A}$.

$\tan 25° = \dfrac{BC}{10}$ *[1 mark]*

$BC = 10 \times \tan 25° = 4.663... = \textbf{4.7 cm}$ (1 d.p.) *[1 mark]*

[4 marks available in total — as above]

7 $\dfrac{6}{2} = 3$, so Z is 3 times larger than Y.
As the triangles are similar, all the angles are the same.

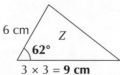

[2 marks available — 1 mark for each correct label]

Section Five — Probability and Statistics

Page 68 — Before you Start

1 a) P(not early) = 1 – P(early) = 1 – 0.1 = **0.9**

b) P(on time) = 1 – P(late) – P(early)
$$= 1 - 0.4 - 0.1 = \mathbf{0.5}$$

2 a) **1, 2, 4, 5, 10**

b)
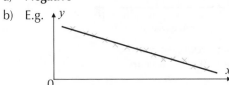

3 a) **Negative**

b) E.g.
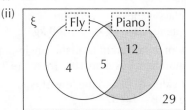

4 a) Mean = total ÷ 5, so 5 = total ÷ 5
Total = 5 × 5 = 25
So 8 + 1 + 2 + x + 6 = 25
x **= 8**

b) 1, 2, 6, 8, 8, 9
So the median is halfway between 6 and 8, i.e. **7**.

Page 69 — Probability from Experiments

1 a) The relative frequency that the spinner lands
on U is 6 ÷ 60 = 0.1. The relative frequency that the
spinner lands on V is 18 ÷ 60 = 0.3. Using the same
method for W and X, the completed table is below.

	U	V	W	X
Frequency	6	18	21	15
Relative frequency	0.1	0.3	0.35	0.25

b) **Biased** — if the spinner were fair, you would expect
the relative frequencies to all be roughly the same
(close to 0.25).
You can see that the spinner is much less likely to land on U.

2 a) $600 \times \frac{1}{3} = \mathbf{200}$

b) $600 \times \frac{2}{5} = \mathbf{240}$

c) $600 \times 1 = \mathbf{600}$
If the probability is 1, the coin is certain to land on heads.
So it will land on heads on every one of the 600 tosses.

3 a) 22 ÷ 40 = **0.55**

b) 40 × 0.35 = **14**

c) The number of people who have won a huge teddy is
40 – 22 – 14 = 4. You can estimate the probability using
the relative frequency: P(huge teddy) ≈ 4 ÷ 40 = **0.1**.
Alternatively, you could use the fact that
mutually exclusive probabilities add up to 1.
So P(huge teddy) ≈ 1 – 0.55 – 0.35 = 0.1.

Pages 70-71 — Theoretical Probability

1 There are 6 + 3 + 9 + 7 = 25 possible sandwiches.

a) P(gluten-free and vegetarian) = $\frac{6}{25}$

b) There are 3 + 7 = 10 sandwiches that are meaty.
P(meaty) = $\frac{10}{25} = \frac{2}{5}$

2 a) The events '3 or lower' and '3 or higher' aren't
mutually exclusive — i.e. they can both happen
at the same time if a 3 is rolled.
Two events are 'mutually exclusive' if they can't both happen at
the same time. For example, a dice landing on 1 and a dice
landing on 2 are mutually exclusive — but a dice landing on
1 and a dice landing on any odd number aren't.

b) There are 12 sides on the dice, so there are 12
possible outcomes of the roll.
$\frac{1}{3} = \frac{4}{12}$, so there are **4 sides** labelled 7.

3 a) Black walls with wood floor
Cream walls with wood floor
Black walls with carpet floor
Cream walls with carpet floor
Black walls with marzipan floor
Cream walls with marzipan floor

b) There are 6 possible outcomes.

(i) P(black walls, carpet floor) = $\frac{1}{6}$

(ii) P(cream walls or marzipan floor) = $\frac{4}{6} = \frac{2}{3}$

4 a) (i) **29**

(ii)
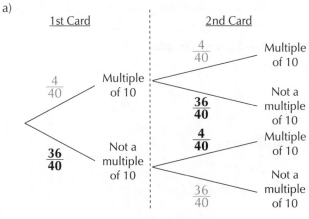

b) (i) 4 + 5 = 9 can fly. P(fly) = $\frac{9}{50}$ = **0.18**

(ii) P(fly and piano) = $\frac{5}{50}$ = **0.1**

5 a)

1st Card   2nd Card

$\frac{4}{40}$ — Multiple of 10

$\frac{4}{40}$ Multiple of 10

$\frac{36}{40}$ — Not a multiple of 10

$\frac{36}{40}$ Not a multiple of 10

$\frac{4}{40}$ — Multiple of 10

$\frac{36}{40}$ — Not a multiple of 10

b) There are now only 3 cards in the bag that are
multiples of 10, and 39 cards in the bag in total.
So the probability is $\frac{3}{39} = \frac{1}{13}$.

Answers

Pages 72-73 — Displaying Data

1

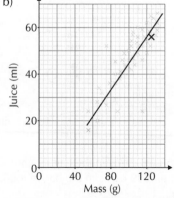

2
```
2 | 6 7 8        Key: 2 | 6 = 26 cm
3 | 5
4 | 1 5 6 8 9
```

3 a)

Speed (s mph)	10 ≤ s < 11	11 ≤ s < 12	12 ≤ s < 13	13 ≤ s < 14
Tally	IIII	II	III	++++
Frequency	**4**	**2**	**3**	**5**

b) *(frequency polygon graph: Frequency vs Speed (mph))*

4 a) Read off the frequency of the point between 100 kg and 200 kg: **12**

b) Add up the frequencies of all the points greater than 400 kg: 10 + 3 + 11 = **24**

c) The modal class is the class with the greatest frequency: **300 kg < m ≤ 400 kg**

5 a) The first row of the diagram is all the single-digit entries (i.e. numbers less than 10). There are **7**.

b) The greatest value is 38 and the lowest is 1, so the range is 38 – 1 = **37**.

c) Look at the left-hand side of the diagram. The highest entry is **27**.

d) 40+: 2, 11, <u>19</u>, 23, 27
Under 40: 3, 5, 6, 11, <u>14</u>, 17, 22, 23, 28
So the 40+ median is greater by 19 – 14 = **5**.

Page 74 — Scatter Graphs

1 a), b) *(scatter graph: Juice (ml) vs Mass (g))*

Read across to the line from 25 ml to find an estimate for the mass: **65 g**
Your line is unlikely to be exactly the same as this one. So long as it slopes upwards and has roughly the same number of points on either side of the line, that's fine. This might mean that your estimate is a bit different — it should be somewhere between 50 g and 70 g.

c) He is **not right** — the graph doesn't show this. You can't use a graph about lemons to draw conclusions about oranges.

2 a) **Negative** correlation — the **older** a hen, the **fewer eggs** it generally lays.

b) *(scatter graph: Number of eggs laid each month vs Age (years))*

c) Oldest = 9, youngest = 1
So range = 9 – 1 = **8 years**

Pages 75-76 — Averages and Range from Tables

1 a) **90 < a ≤ 120**

b) There are 30 values, so the median is between the 15th and 16th values. There are 4 + 3 + 7 = 14 values in the first three classes, so the 15th and 16th values are in the fourth class: **90 < a ≤ 120**

c) (i)

Area (a hectares)	0 < a ≤ 30	30 < a ≤ 60	60 < a ≤ 90	90 < a ≤ 120	120 < a ≤ 150	Total
Frequency (f)	4	3	7	10	6	30
Mid-interval value (m)	**15**	**45**	**75**	**105**	**135**	—
f × m	**60**	**135**	**525**	**1050**	**810**	**2580**

(ii) Mean ≈ 2580 ÷ 30 = **86 hectares**
Use ≈ instead of = here because it's just an estimate.

2 a) 9 – 4 = **5 hours**
Note that the highest value for the number of hours of sleep is 9 (as no one slept for 10 hours).

b) Total frequency = 20
So the median is between the 10th and 11th values. There are 3 + 4 + 6 = 13 values in the first three columns, but 3 + 4 = 7 values in the first two columns, so the 10th and 11th values are in the third column. So the median is **6 hours**.

c) The mode is the number of hours that has the highest frequency: 6 hours. For the mean, work out (number of hours) × (frequency) for each column: 12, 20, 36, 35, 8, 9, 0.
Then the sum of these is 120.
Mean = 120 ÷ 20 = 6 hours.
Yes, they are correct — the mode and the mean are the same.

3 a) Total frequency = 14
So the median is between the 7th and 8th values. There are 4 + 2 = 6 values in the first two groups, so the 7th and 8th values are in the third group: **6 - 7**.

b) To find the smallest range, subtract the largest possible 'least value' from the smallest possible 'greatest value'. This is 8 – 3 = **5**.

Answers

4 a) (i) To find the maximum possible range, subtract the smallest possible 'least value' from the largest possible 'greatest value'.
This is 100 – 20 = **80 seconds**.

(ii) If the greatest value was fixed at 89, the maximum possible range would be 89 – 20 = **69 seconds**.

b) (i) Add some extra columns to the table:

Time (t seconds)	Frequency	Mid-interval value (m)	$f \times m$
$20 \leq t < 40$	9	30	270
$40 \leq t < 60$	14	50	700
$60 \leq t < 80$	11	70	770
$80 \leq t < 100$	6	90	540
Total	40	—	2280

Mean ≈ 2280 ÷ 40 = **57 seconds**

(ii) E.g. you don't know the actual data values (only the classes that they're in).

Pages 77-78 — Review Exercise

1 a) There are 17 entries in the diagram, so **17 pupils**. *[1 mark]*

b) 50 – 14 = **36** *[1 mark]*

c) The median is the 9th value: 30.
The mode is the value with the most entries: 36.
So the difference is 36 – 30 = **6**.
[2 marks available — 1 mark for correctly identifying either the median or the mode, 1 mark for the correct final answer]

2 a) E.g. **disagree** — the correlation isn't strong. *[1 mark]*
There is positive correlation, but the points are quite spread out, so it's moderate or weak positive correlation.

b) **310 kg** *[1 mark]*
Allow any mass between 310 kg and 314 kg.

c) **10 cm**, **300 kg** and **49 cm**, **190 kg**
[2 marks available — 2 marks for all correct, otherwise 1 mark for both lengths correct or both masses correct or one pair of length and mass correct]

3 a) Relative frequency of 4 = 6 ÷ 50 = 0.12
So P(4) ≈ **0.12**. *[1 mark]*

b) 0.2 × 80 = **16** *[1 mark]*

4 The probabilities of all the outcomes add up to 1.
So P(1) + 0.2 + 0.5 + P(4) = 1 $\Rightarrow$ P(1) + P(4) = 0.3
But P(1) = 2 × P(4), so 2P(4) + P(4) = 0.3.
3P(4) = 0.3, so P(4) = 0.1
P(1) = 2P(4) = 2 × 0.1 = **0.2**
[2 marks available — 2 marks for the correct answer, otherwise 1 mark for knowing that the two missing probabilities add up to 0.3]

5 a)

Length (l miles)	$0 < l \leq 10$	$10 < l \leq 20$	$20 < l \leq 30$	$30 < l \leq 40$	$40 < l \leq 50$	$50 < l \leq 60$
Frequency	14	8	11	4	2	3

[2 marks available — 2 marks for a fully correct table, otherwise 1 mark for at least four entries correct]

b) Extend the table:

Mid-interval value (m)	5	15	25	35	45	55
$m \times f$	70	120	275	140	90	165

Total of frequency = 42
Total of $m \times f$ = 860
Mean ≈ 860 ÷ 42 = 20.476...
= **20 miles** (to nearest mile)
[3 marks available — 1 mark for calculating the mid-interval values, 1 mark for calculating $m \times f$, 1 mark for the correct final answer]

Topic Map

There's a whole bunch of maths to learn at <u>Key Stage 3</u> — and different schools teach the content in <u>different orders</u>. This table shows you where we <u>introduce</u> each of the topics from the curriculum.

	Year 7 Workbook	Year 8 Workbook	Year 9 Workbook
Section One — Number	**Place value and ordering numbers**		
	Addition and subtraction — whole numbers, decimals	**Addition and subtraction —** harder decimals, negative numbers	**Solving number problems —** using non-calculator arithmetic
	Multiplication and division — powers of 10, whole numbers	**Multiplication and division —** decimals, negative numbers	
	Negative numbers — ordering, simple addition	**Negative numbers —** harder calculations	
	BODMAS — brackets, division, multiplication, addition, subtraction	**BODMAS —** brackets, powers and roots, division, multiplication, addition, subtraction	
	Inverse operations		
	Rounding — to the nearest 10, 100, 1000, etc., to the nearest whole number	**Rounding —** decimal places, significant figures	**Rounding —** rounding errors, inequality notation
	Estimating — by rounding to whole numbers or to the nearest 10, 100, 1000, etc.	**Estimating —** by rounding to 1 significant figure	**Estimating —** solving problems by rounding to specified accuracy
	Powers and roots — squares, square roots, cubes, cube roots	**Powers and roots —** higher powers, powers of 10, approximating roots	**Power and roots —** power laws, negative powers
			Standard form
	Multiples and LCM		
	Factors and HCF		
	Prime numbers — identifying primes	**Prime factorisation —** factor trees, product notation	**Prime factorisation —** using prime factors to find e.g. LCM, HCF, squares, roots
Section Two — Proportions and Units	**Fraction basics —** equivalent fractions, ordering fractions, mixed numbers, improper fractions		**Solving fraction problems**
	Adding and subtracting fractions — denominators with a common factor	**Adding and subtracting fractions —** denominators with no common factors	
	Multiplying fractions — by whole numbers	**Multiplying fractions —** by other fractions	
		Dividing fractions	
	Fractions, decimals, percentages — simple converting without a calculator	**Fractions, decimals, percentages —** harder converting, comparing proportions	
	Percentages of amounts — with and without a calculator	**Percentages of amounts —** solving harder problems	
		Percentage change — finding new amounts	**Percentage change —** finding the percentage change, finding the original amount, simple interest, harder problems
	Ratios — introducing ratio notation, simplifying ratios	**Ratios —** harder simplifying, writing in the form $1:n$, solving ratio problems	**Ratios —** decimals, mixed units, harder ratio problems
	Proportion — comparing amounts using fractions, percentages and ratios	**Proportion —** scaling up and down	**Proportion —** direct and inverse proportion, harder scaling problems, algebra and graphs
	Time — converting between the 12- and 24-hour clock, units of time, timetables		
		Compound measures — speed problems	**Compound measures —** harder speed problems, density problems, best buy problems
	Units — using metric units, converting between metric units	**Units —** converting between metric and imperial units	**Units —** converting compound units, including areas and volumes
		Scales and scale drawings — converting and drawing using simple scales	**Scales and scale drawings —** scales given as ratios